SUNS, MYTHS AND MEN

SUNS, MYTHS AND MEN

Patrick Moore, F.R.A.S.

FREDERICK MULLER

First published in Great Britain 1954
by Frederick Muller Ltd., Fleet Street, London, E.C.4.

Copyright © 1954, 1968 Patrick Moore

Completely revised edition 1968

Phototypeset by BAS Printers Ltd., Wallop, Hampshire
Printed by Fleming and Humphreys (Baylis) Ltd,
Leicester
and bound by
Leighton-Straker Bookbinding Co. Ltd., London, N.W.10

CONTENTS

PART III: THE FUTURE

ILLUSTRATIONS

FOREWORD

THE FIRST EDITION of this book was published in 1954, which means that it was actually written in 1953. In those days, the Space Age had not begun, and rocket research was not taken very seriously except by the comparative few who were actively engaged in it. When I was invited to bring the book up to date, I realized that extensive re-writing would be needed; by the time I had finished, I had written what is in fact a new book, though I retained the original pattern as far as possible. My thanks are due to Geoffrey Piper, of Messrs. Frederick Muller, who suggested the revision and has been of the greatest help to me throughout.

The line drawings were executed by Lawrence Clarke, to whom I am most grateful.

PATRICK MOORE

The Planetarium,
Armagh. February 1968.

INTRODUCTION

ASTRONOMY IS A fast-developing science. It is seldom
nowadays that a year passes by without some spectacular new advance, and it is not at all easy to keep
up to date. Yet this is a new departure; at the start
of the present century the rate of progress was
much gentler, while a few hundred years ago
astronomy was to all intents and purposes static.

Without trying to draw any hard and fast bound-
aries, it is probably true to say that there have been
three main phases. The first was that of myth,
astrology and a little science; it began with our
remote cave-dwelling ancestors, and ended in
mediæval times. Then came the great change, with
the Earth removed from its pre-eminent position in
the centre of the universe and relegated to the
status of a perfectly ordinary planet. Finally, since
the earlier part of the nineteenth century, there
has been what we may term the modern era. The
Space Age, which began on 4 October 1957 with the
launching of Russia's first artificial satellite, is
now under way, but as yet we have not seen more
than the first results of it.

In this book I propose to compare the astronomy

of these basic periods, and to speculate as to what is likely to happen in the future. It has often been said that comparisons are odious, but this can hardly apply in the astronomical sense, and there is surely something to be learned from comparing our present-day ideas with those of the past. The chief lesson seems to be that the more we find out, the more we realize how little we really know.

Part I

THE PAST

The Earth's Beginning

LOOK UP INTO the sky on any clear night, and you will see several thousands of stars. If you use binoculars, the number of visible stars will be increased tremendously; if a telescope is available, the total star-count runs into millions. Each star is a sun, and there must be something like 100,000 million suns in our own particular star-system or Galaxy. Beyond, in the depths of space, there are other galaxies, some of them considerably larger than the system in which we live.

Endless discussions have taken place about what is usually called "the origin of the universe". The material making up the Earth, the Sun and the galaxies must have come from somewhere, but our knowledge of the Creation is a complete blank, and no sensible person, scientist or layman, will pretend otherwise. So far as the origin of the Earth is concerned, we are rather better informed, even though no theory yet put forward is convincing enough to satisfy everybody.

At least we have a reasonably good idea of our time-scale. It is believed that the Earth began its separate existence about 4,700,000,000 years ago, and

The Great Bear, photographed with an exposure of 2 hrs. 30 mins.

this figure is certainly of the right order, even though there is an obvious uncertainty of a good many millions of years either way. There are several lines of investigation, all of which lead to the same result. For instance, there is the method of radio-activity, which is independent of outside influences such as changes in temperature, and which provides a convenient measuring-clock.

There are some substances which decay, quite
spontaneously, into different materials. The
heaviest of all the elements known to occur naturally is uranium; over immense periods this uranium
"breaks down", and ends its career as uranium-
lead. If, therefore, we find uranium and uranium-
lead together, the ratio of the one substance to the
other tells us how long the decaying process has
been going on. Since uranium is found in some
rocks, we have a key to the ages of the rocks themselves. There are all sorts of complications to be
taken into account, but the basic idea is quite
straightforward.

Another element that decays in similar fashion is
rubidium, which ends up as a totally different
element, strontium. It takes 46,000 million years for

Star trails near the North Pole

any piece of rubidium to turn half of itself into strontium, so that the change is leisurely by any standards, but it can be measured. Between Africa and South America lie the Rocks of St. Paul, which contain rubidium, and whose age has been measured as about 4,500 million years. This gives us a lower limit to the age of the Earth, and it seems safe to assume that 5,000 million years is the extreme upper limit, so that we have been presented with our first clue.

In whatever manner the Earth were formed, the Sun must certainly have played an important rôle. An attractive theory, popular not so very long ago, was that a passing star pulled a long tongue of matter out of the Sun, and that the Earth and the other planets condensed out of this material—which sounds logical enough; the Sun, like all stars, is a globe of incandescent gas, and the effects of a more massive star passing close by would be violent indeed. Unfortunately, the mathematical objections to the theory are so strong that nearly all scientists have now abandoned it, albeit with regret. It is more likely that the planets were formed from material collected by the Sun during its passage through a gas-and-dust cloud in space, as is supposed by the German physicist Carl von Weizsäcker. Probably all the planets came into existence at about the same time, and in the same way. This applies also to the Moon, which is best regarded as a secondary planet rather than as our satellite.

The earliest part of the Earth's history need not concern us at the moment. Suffice to say that according to available evidence the world went through a "hot" period, during which it lost its original atmosphere, and then cooled down, producing a new atmosphere made up of gases expelled from inside the globe. As the temperature dropped, and the crust solidified, conditions started to become suitable for the appearance of life.

Here, too, our ideas have changed during the modern period. During the seventeenth century, the Church authorities officially supported Archbishop Ussher of Armagh, who maintained that the world had come into existence at ten o'clock in the morning of 26 October, 4004 B.C. The Archbishop had

IACOBVS VSSERIVS
EPISC: ARMACHANVS

Archbishop Ussher of Armagh, who gave the date of the Earth's creation as 4004 B.C.

arrived at this precise figure by adding up the ages of the Patriarchs in the Old Testament, and making some equally irrelevant calculations. Theologians were satisfied, but scientists were not, and it soon became clear that many fossils—that is to say, the

remains of plants and animals embedded in rocks—
were much older than 4004 B.C., or, for that matter,
4,000,004 B.C. Latest estimates trace living creatures
back to the so-called Pre-Cambrian period, which
began with the formation of the Earth and ended
some 600 million years ago.

Early life was humble enough, and took the form
of tiny single-celled creatures living in the sea. We
have to admit that we do not know just how life
started, but at least we may be sure that it was
extremely slow to develop. Between 600 and 500
million years ago there were seaweeds and jellyfish
in the warm oceans, together with worms, primitive
starfishes and many other small creatures which
have long since become extinct. At that time the
world bore little resemblance to the world of today;
Great Britain was under water, and so were parts of
the modern United States, while the huge continent
of Gondwanaland spread across what are now South
America, the Atlantic, Africa and the Indian Ocean.

There was another striking difference, too, inasmuch as the atmosphere was unbreathable by our
standards. It contained large quantities of the
heavy gas carbon dioxide, but relatively little free
oxygen, so that a modern man who could board a
time-machine and send himself back 500 million
years into the past would promptly choke. It was
not until later that plants spread on to the barren,
inhospitable continents, and caused a change in the
air. Reduced to its simplest terms, we may say that
plants "take in" carbon dioxide and send out oxygen,
while all animals, including men, do the reverse;
we breathe in oxygen, and expel carbon dioxide.
Once the plants had obtained a foothold on the
continents, they removed much of the carbon

dioxide, and made it possible for animal life to develop. Needless to say, this process was far from rapid, and it was not until between 400 and 350 million years ago that the first land-creatures appeared on the scene. They were amphibians, spending much of their lives in the water, but they were immensely significant. By that time fishes were plentiful in the oceans, and there were large numbers of sharks.

From fishes to amphibians; from amphibians to reptiles. During what is known as the Mesozoic era, which extended from about 225 to only 70 million years ago, vegetation was abundant and generally luxuriant, while the world was dominated by huge reptiles of which the ferocious, flesh-eating dinosaurs are best remembered. Their skeletons may be seen in many museums, and they were certainly the most terrifying creatures ever to have existed on Earth, but they were not notable for their intelligence. Even the tyrannosaurus, which stood almost 20 ft. high and had a total length of 40 ft., was less intelligent than a kitten. Not all the dinosaurs were flesh-eaters; some were harmless enough, and a few types, such as the pterodactyls, took to the air in an attempt to keep out of harm's way, though they were not flyers in the modern sense.

About 70 million years ago the dinosaurs died out, rather suddenly on the time-scale of Earth history, and for reasons about which we are still rather uncertain. It may well be that the climatic changes of the period were too much for them, and that the vast reptiles, with their clumsy bodies and negligible brains, simply could not adapt themselves. At any rate, they vanished; and with their disappearance, warm-blooded mammals could develop.

The Age of Mammals, then, began 70 million years ago. This may sound a long time, but it is only about one-seventieth of the total age of the Earth, so that the mammals may be regarded as comparative newcomers. From their modest beginnings they evolved slowly but steadily; the strange, rabbit-sized animal known as the eohippus developed into the modern horse, and so on. And some particular mammals known as the primates, which dwelt in trees at the start of the era, have evolved into monkeys, apes and men.

How often has it been taught that, according to Darwin's theory of evolution, men are descended from monkeys? More times than can be counted; but nothing could be further from the truth, and Charles Darwin, the great naturalist, would have been the last to maintain anything of the sort. It is quite correct to say that monkeys, apes, men and various small modern primates, such as the lemurs, have common ancestry, but that is all. Some branches of the original primates evolved into animals such as monkeys, while other branches produced men. There has never been any serious suggestion that apes or monkeys will develop further, or that their future descendants will acquire human intelligence. They are distant relatives of ours, but they belong to a completely different line.

Another common mistake is worth noting. When true men appeared on Earth, vegetation was of modern type, and the world map was not very different from that of today (though there were differences in detail; for instance, Britain was joined on to the European mainland, and there was no Channel). There were animals which have since died out, such as the sabre-toothed tiger, the mammoth and the mastodon. Early men hunted the mammoth, and may indeed have been largely responsible for its destruction, just as the great auk and the American passenger pigeon were exterminated much later. But the great dinosaurs had vanished tens of millions of years before, and the comic-strip cartoons which show Mr. and Mrs. B.C. locking up their cave and putting the brontosaurus out for the night are grotesquely wide of the mark.

The period known to geologists as the Pleistocene began roughly a million years ago, and ended 10,000 years ago, which may be called 8000 B.C. by historical reckoning. This was the time of the last Ice Age, when the average temperature of the Earth was appreciably lower than it is now. There have been Ice Ages now and then all through geological records, and the Pleistocene glacial was merely the last of them, but it has left its mark, and has been well studied. There were four cold waves, separated by warmer periods or interglacials. It has been suggested that we are today living during an interglacial, and that eventually the cold may return, which is quite possible even though we have no proof. We cannot even be sure of the causes of the Ice Age; it is logical to suppose that slight fluctuations in the output of light and heat from the Sun were responsible, but in any case the temperature on Earth was still sufficiently high for men to exist, and we have a reasonably good idea of the Pleistocene way of life.

There is no doubt that the ape-like creature known as Australopithecus flourished a million years ago, and that it had sufficient intelligence to chip stone for use in cutting up animals which had been killed for food. Whether creatures of this sort may be classed as real men is a matter for debate, but in any case *homo sapiens* made his entry long before the final retreat of the ice 10,000 years ago. Recently, discoveries in Africa, where the first men seem to have lived, have pushed the story of humanity back even further; but these investigations, fascinating though they are, are beyond the scope of this book.

Some branches of primitive humanity died out without leaving descendants, while others survived and evolved. The Neanderthal men, so named because a skull of one of them was found in a cave at Neanderthal (near Düsseldorf) in 1856, must have lived in what is now Europe for thousands of years, and developed a definite culture, since they wore skin clothing, buried their dead and knew about fire. They walked more or less upright, but their jaw-structures show that they were not capable of speech as we know it. The Cro-Magnon men, who lived at the same period, were of a much higher order, and could presumably talk, at least in their own fashion. It may be that they made war against the Neanderthalers, or it may be that the Neanderthal type merely died out; our knowledge is still hopelessly patchy, and there is no conclusive evidence that the Cro-Magnon men were our own direct ancestors. All we can say is that the world at the end of the Ice Age was a suitable place for civilizations to develop.

Anthropology, "the science of man", is handicapped by a lack of written records, and it is only too easy to be deceived. This is shown, surely, by the story of the Piltdown Man, which has caused an immense amount of trouble. In 1911 an ape-man's skull was unearthed at the little Sussex village of Piltdown, and further discoveries led scientists to name the creature Eoanthropus, or Dawn-Man; it was thought that the age must be about 200,000 years, and that Eoanthropus was unique in our experience. Eventually, modern-type tests showed that the Piltdown specimen consisted of a moderately ancient skull together with parts of a monkey which had been alive only a century or so earlier. The hoax was deliberate enough, and it was definitely not appreciated in scientific circles, so that most anthropologists prefer to forget it. The site of the "discovery" has been officially removed from the list of Ancient Monuments, though the local public-house is still called *The Piltdown Man.* . . .

Present-day techniques ensure that hoaxes of the Piltdown type cannot be repeated, but with the development of writing we come to the period covered by archæology, and obviously we are much better informed. We know how in some parts of the world men gave up their nomadic ways of life and became farmers and settlers; the Old Stone Age gave way to something quite different, and permanent townships grew up to replace the cave-dwellings. The last cold spell of the Ice Age ended, and nations arose.

One of the first of all historical characters was King Menes, who became ruler of all Egypt and founded the city of Memphis. Apparently he began his reign about 4000 B.C.; he drew up a code of laws, waged successful military campaigns and unified his country, ruling successfully for sixty years before he was unfortunate enough to be killed by a hippopotamus. With Menes, we must leave the story of mankind to the archæologists and historians, since almost everyone has heard of the ancient civilizations such as Sumeria, China and Egypt, and for the moment I propose to confine myself to the development of astronomical thought.

So far as the Ice Age peoples were concerned, there can be little to be said, though there is no harm in making some guesses. Of course they thought the Earth to be flat, and to lie in the centre of the universe, with the sky turning round it once a day. It would have been unreasonable for them to suppose otherwise, and they could know nothing whatsoever about the nature of the stars. Yet even the earliest human beings must have looked upward, and wondered at what they saw.

[2]

What is the World?

DURING THE SECOND century A.D., Claudius Ptole-
mæus of Alexandria—more generally known to us
as Ptolemy—drew up a map of the world. It was
distorted and incomplete, but many places can be
identified, and Great Britain is clearly shown, even
though Ptolemy did join Scotland on to England in
a sort of back-to-front position. All things considered, the map was a remarkable achievement,
and it was constructed according to the best scientific principles of the time, so that it was something
much more important than mere guesswork.
Ptolemy was the last of the great thinkers of the
Classical period, and, of course, he knew quite well
that the Earth is a globe instead of being flat. His
only major error was in supposing that the Earth
must lie in the centre of the universe.

We know nothing about Ptolemy's personality or
life-story, but of his brilliance there can be no doubt
whatsoever, and his book, the *Almagest* (the title is
Arabic; Ptolemy's original has not come down to us)
is a full summary of astronomy as he knew it.
There had already been ample time for development.
Four thousand years separated Ptolemy from King

Menes of Egypt, but less than two thousand years lie between Ptolemy and ourselves.

Naturally, the various civilizations that arose, matured and decayed during ancient times produced very different pictures of the universe, and it is interesting to look back at some of them, not necessarily in chronological order. There was no true understanding of the nature of things, but what we must not do, on any account, is to laugh. The old ideas seem quaint enough nowadays, but they were perfectly rational then.

The Egyptians were remarkable people, and they were capable of carrying out very accurate measurements, but they made an initial mistake in supposing that the universe takes the form of a rectangular box, with the longer sides running north-south. There was a flat ceiling, supported by four pillars at the cardinal points, and the pillars were connected by a mountain chain, below which lay a ledge containing the celestial river Ur-nes. Along this river sailed the boats carrying the Sun and other gods. The people of the eastern cities of the Nile Delta even thought that the heavens were formed by the body of the goddess Nut, who was permanently suspended in what must have been an uncomfortable as well as an inelegant position. Egypt lay in the centre of the flat Earth, and was surrounded on all sides by a vast ocean.

Equally strange was their idea of how the bodies in the sky moved. It was thought that the Sun, Moon and stars travelled round the Earth in square paths, so that when a body came to a corner it turned sharply at right angles.

On the other hand, the Egyptians had an adequate calendar of 365 days, and they paid great attention to the "heliacal rising" of Sirius—that is to say, the time in each year when Sirius, the brightest star in the sky, could first be seen in the dawn light. A calendar was absolutely necessary, because the whole of Egyptian economy was dependent upon the annual flooding of the Nile, and it was essential to know when the flooding could be expected. Also, they divided the stars into definite groups or constellations. These groups were different from our own, but they were just as good, and had history followed a different line we might today be using the Egyptian constellations instead of the Greek ones.

Moreover, the Egyptians were deeply concerned with time-measurement. Each day and each night was divided into twelve hours, so that the hours had different lengths according to the season of the year. The system was clumsy and inconvenient, but it could be made to work, and it lasted for many centuries. Sun-clocks and water-clocks were in use, and gave reasonably accurate results.

The famous Pyramids are astronomically aligned, and the literature about them is voluminous. For our present purpose it will be enough to make brief mention of just one aspect, concerning the Great Pyramid of Cheops—included among the Seven Wonders of the World, and still to be seen in all its magnificence. The Great Pyramid was built about 3000 B.C. The date of its construction can be worked out quite accurately, because its main passage was oriented with respect to the north pole of the sky, and the polar point in those days was not the same as it is now.

We of the twentieth century know that the Earth is a globe, rotating on its axis once a day, and that the axis points northward to a position marked closely by Polaris, the Pole Star. There is an effect known as precession, making the pole describe a circle in the sky over a period of about 26,000 years; it is due to the fact that the Earth is not perfectly spherical, but has an equatorial "bulge" which is acted on by the gravitational pull of the Sun and Moon. As it spins, the Earth topples slightly, in the manner of a gyroscope which is running down. By everyday standards the effect is very small, but over the centuries it mounts up, and can be measured without any difficulty. Reckoning backwards in time, we find that when Cheops' labourers were building the Pyramid the north pole of the sky lay not near Polaris, but near a much fainter star, Thuban in the constellation of the Dragon. Therefore, Thuban was the Pole Star of Ancient Egypt. When all the necessary corrections have been made, it is found that the lining-up of the Great Pyramid is amazingly accurate.

The Pyramid is an architectural masterpiece, but nothing more, and the cult of Pyramidology, which flourished in the last century and was supported by no less an authority than the then Astronomer Royal for Scotland, is quite baseless. (Pyramidologists set out to prove that the various dimensions of the Pyramid were calculated in the form of a code, and that this code can give the key to events in both the past and the future. Their earnest researches make amusing reading now.)

The idea of an Earth standing on pillars was also popular with the Chinese, who thought that the world must have a square base even though the heavens were round. The Babylonians held that the Earth arose from water, possibly because deposits of silt seem to make lands rise from the sea. To them, the sky was solid, so that each day the Sun rose by entering through a door in the east, and set in the evening through another door in the west. The Earth itself was an immense hollow mountain, divided into four quadrants, of which the northern was unknown and mysterious; between heaven and Earth extended the waters of the eastern and western oceans, which, like the southern ocean, were parts of Apsu, the Great Deep which supported the flat Earth. Inside the mountain lay the abode of the dead, with its entrance toward the west. It was thought likely that the gods lived upon the top of the mountain.

We can pass briefly over the ideas of the Hebrews, merely mentioning that they, too, supposed the Earth to be supported on pillars. The Indians, however, took matters rather further. By some tribes it was thought that the Earth was carried on the shoulders of elephants, while the elephants were in turn supported by a huge turtle swimming in a limitless sea. In Vedic lore, the flat universe was made up of concentric rings, alternately land and sea; the central island was the Earth, and was divided into four quarters, of which the southern was India. At the centre of the Earth lay the tall mountain Meru, around which the celestial bodies revolved in horizontal orbits at different heights. The outermost sea was surrounded by a chain of peaks, and no sunrays could penetrate beyond, so that the outer land was deserted and always dark. As in many other beliefs, the sky was thought to be solid.

Then there was the terrace theory of the Hindus, according to which the Earth took the form of a pyramid, sloping down from the valley of Tibet, again from the Himalayas to the Ganges Valley, yet again to the plauteau of Central India, and finally to the sea on the south, so making up a series of successive terraces. On the top of the pyramid was Mount Meru, dwelling-place of the gods, which was "golden and shining like fire which is not dulled by smoke . . . it had four different colours on its four different sides. Around the mountain lay a pond, and around it to all sides were the guardians of the world". The Hindu universe was bounded by vertical walls, beyond which there was nothing but darkness.

All this sounds fanciful enough, but the theories of the earliest of the Greek philosophers were not much better, and it seems that they had simply taken over some of the ideas of the Babylonians. Thales of Miletus, first of the philosophers, lived from about 624 to 547 B.C. The story which relates how he walked into a deep well while gazing upward at the stars seems to be fairly well authenticated, and certainly he paid great attention to astronomy, but he seems to have believed the Earth to be flat, and he taught that the world floated on water in the manner of a log or cork. To Thales, water was the most important of all substances, and earth was produced by its condensation, while fire was nothing more than heated air which was also of watery origin. Anaximander, his younger contemporary, held that the Earth is a short cylinder, one of its two plane faces being that on which we stand. The stars were in the nature of fiery jets, and Anaximander wrote that the Sun "is like a chariot-wheel, the rim of which is hollow and full of fire, letting the fire shine out at a certain point in it like the nozzle of a pair of bellows".

On the credit side, Anaximander claimed that the Earth is suspended freely in space, and that it remains in this position because it is at an equal distance from all the rest of the celestial bodies. He can have had no conception of what we call "gravity", but it may be said that the germ of the idea is there. At any rate, his scheme was better than that of Anaximenes of Miletus, who taught that the Earth is supported by the air, and that the stars are fastened on to a crystal sphere.

Then, somewhat later, came Pythagoras. Nowadays Pythagoras is known as the author of a famous geometrical theorem,[1] but he was much more than that. He seems to have known that the Earth is a globe, and presumably he also thought the same about the Sun and Moon. Unfortunately we know relatively little about his astronomical work, but he certainly spent some time in Egypt, so that he was familiar with Egyptian theories, and he realized that the stars are quite different in character from the five "wandering stars" or planets, known today as Mercury, Venus, Mars, Jupiter and Saturn. Pythagoras accepted the idea of a solid sphere with the stars fixed to it, but he was well in advance of his contemporary Xenophanes, who thought that the world had been born from a mixture of earth and water, and will come to an end when it is absorbed back into the sea and changed into mud. According to Xenophanes, there is a new sun every day, while the Earth's flat upper side touches the air and its lower side extends without limit. And Heraclitus of Ephesus, who was born about 544 B.C., taught that the Sun can be no

---

[1] The square on the hypotenuse of a right-angled triangle is equal to the sum of the squares on the other two sides.

more than twelve inches in diameter.

There were many other Greek philosophers in the centuries following Thales, but before we come to Aristotle, who may be said to have killed the flat earth theory, we must pause to mention Empedocles and Anaxagoras. Empedocles thought that the universe is shaped like an egg, with the stars attached to a crystal sphere. Inside this sphere was a second sphere made up of two halves, one of which was full of fire while the other was chiefly air; these two hemispheres moved around the Earth, so producing day and night—day when the fire-half was in view, night when the air-half was above. The Sun was nothing more than a reflection of the light from the fire-sphere. Anaxagoras, born around 500 B.C., was a flat-earth supporter, but he was bold enough to suggest that the Sun is a red-hot stone larger than the peninsula in which Athens lies. This led him into trouble with the authorities, and his case provides an early instance of science v. orthodox religion. He was not put to death, but he was banished from Athens, and never returned to the city. But for his friendship with Pericles, the most powerful Athenian politician of the time, he might have fared much worse.

Aristotle's life extended from about 384 to 322 B.C. His reputation became so great that to question his theories was regarded as heretical, and it was fortunate for astronomy that he came to the conclusion that the flat-earth theory must be wrong. He reasoned that the sphere is "the shape that a body naturally assumes when all parts of it tend toward the centre"; again we have the first glimmerings about gravitation. Secondly, Aristotle made the point that the altitudes of stars change according to the position of the observer; Polaris, for instance, is higher up as seen from Greece than from Egypt, and Canopus, the brilliant southern star, rises from Alexandria but not from Athens. This sort of thing is only to be expected if the Earth is a globe, but it cannot possibly be accounted for if the Earth is assumed to be flat.

Aristotle's third proof was associated with eclipses of the Moon. It was already known that the Moon has no light of its own, but depends entirely upon reflecting sunlight, in the manner of a large though inefficient mirror (actually, the Moon's albedo, or reflecting power, is a mere 7 per cent). When the Moon passes into the shadow of the Earth its direct supply of sunlight is cut off, and the Earth's shadow can be seen on the lunar disk. Aristotle pointed out that as this shadow is curved, the surface of the Earth must also be curved.

All this seemed conclusive enough. Aristotle had taught that the world was round, and so round it must be. The next problem was to measure its size, and this was done by Eratosthenes of Cyrene, who flourished about 200 B.C.

In principle, Eratosthenes' method was very simple and completely sound. It was based on the fact that when the Sun is directly overhead from one observing site, it is some way from the overhead point as seen from another station. The sites chosen by Eratosthenes were Alexandria, where he lived, and Syene (the modern Assouan), some way up the Nile.

At the time of the summer solstice—that is to say, the time when the Sun reaches its northernmost point in its annual journey round the sky, in mid-June each year—the noon sun at Syene is exactly overhead, as Eratosthenes learned from a study of the books in the great Alexandrian Library of which he was in charge. From Alexandria, however, the Sun is not exactly overhead at this moment,

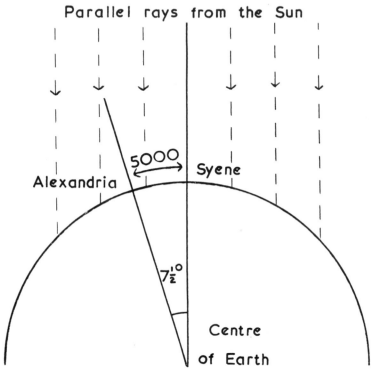

ERATOSTHENES' METHOD OF MEASURING THE SIZE OF THE EARTH. When the Sun shone overhead at Syene, it was 7½ degrees from the overhead point as seen from Alexandria. The distance from Syene to Alexandria was known to be 5,000 stadia, and from this information Eratosthenes was able to calculate the Earth's size with remarkable accuracy. For the sake of clarity, the drawing is not to scale

and by careful measurement Eratosthenes found that the distance from the zenith or overhead point was 7½ degrees. A full circle contains 360 degrees, and 7½ is about one-fiftieth of 360, so that if the Earth is spherical its circumference must be fifty times the distance between Alexandria and Syene.

The next task was to find the distance between the two towns, and this was not so easy as might be thought, since map-making had hardly begun and no reliable charts were available. According to a story which may or may not be true, Eratosthenes solved the problem by driving from Alexandria to Syene in his coach, and estimating the distance by counting the number of turns made by his coach-wheel. The distance proved to be 5,000 stadia, and it followed that the Earth's circumference must be 250,000 stadia.

The stadion is an ancient measure of distance, but unfortunately there were several varieties of it. Since we are not sure which stadion Eratosthenes used we cannot tell the final accuracy of his estimate. However, one value for the stadion is 517 ft., and in this case the Earth's circumference would come out at 24,850 miles and its diameter at 7,850 miles. The true figures are 24,900 miles and 7,926 miles respectively. In any case, Eratosthenes was amazingly accurate, and his result remained the best for over a thousand years. It was much nearer the truth than the value taken by Christopher Columbus during his voyage to the New World in 1492; Columbus thought that the circumference of the Earth was less than 19,000 miles, which explains why he failed to realize that he had discovered a previously unknown land-mass instead of arriving at his intended target of Asia.

To use a hackneyed modern term, the discovery
that the Earth is a globe about 8,000 miles in
diameter was the first great "break-through" in
astronomy. Note that it was achieved not by guesswork, but by sound scientific reasoning, which is
where the Greeks—at any rate, the later ones—were
so much in advance of the Chinese, the Egyptians,
the Babylonians and the rest. Aristotle did not
simply assume the Earth to be spherical; he demonstrated it by observation. And nobody can fault
Eratosthenes, either in his method or in the way in
which he applied it.

The Greeks very nearly managed the second
break-through: the discovery that instead of being
the centre of the universe, the Earth is an ordinary
planet moving round the Sun. Aristarchus of Samos,
who lived from about 310 to 230 B.C:, put forward
precisely this idea, and he also gave the Sun's
distance as 5,000,000 miles, which was a gallant
attempt even though much too small. Aristarchus'
method for measuring the Earth–Sun distance need
not concern us at the moment, but it was perfectly
correct in theory, and the only trouble was that it
was virtually impossible to apply with any accuracy.

It was unfortunate that Aristarchus' views did
not become popular, and were disregarded by the
two great astronomers of late Classical times.
Hipparchus (about 170 to 120 B.C.) went back to the
ideas of Aristotle, even though he was a brilliant
observer who drew up an excellent star-catalogue
and increased the distance of the Sun to 10,000,000
miles. Last of all came Ptolemy, who brought
ancient astronomy to its highest degree of perfection but who also continued to believe in a
central Earth. Until less than five hundred years

ago Ptolemy and Aristotle were still regarded as the supreme authorities with regard to the mechanics of the universe.

Yet astronomy at the time of Ptolemy's death in A.D. 180 was something very different from the vague fancies of earlier years. Quite apart from the revised ideas about the Earth, the movements of the planets and other bodies in the sky had been measured very carefully, and Hipparchus had even discovered precession, which shows how good an observer he must have been. On the other hand, there were still the intellectual obstacles of myth, religion and astrology. The real nature of the universe remained a puzzle, and astronomy was not yet a clear-cut science on its own account.

[3]

Suns and Gods

> You have made the far skies so that you may shine in them,
> Your disk in its solitude looks on all that you have made,
> Appearing in its glory and gleaming both near and far.
> Out of your singleness you shape a million forms—
> Towns and villages, fields, roads and the river.
> All eyes behold you, bright Disk of the day.

THESE LINES COME from one of the oldest hymns in the world: the Hymn to the Sun, composed by Akhenaten, the extraordinary Egyptian Pharaoh who founded a religion based upon sun-worship and kindliness. Akhenaten began his reign in or about 1367 B.C. He was young, possibly still in his teens, and we do not know quite how long he ruled, though we do know that in the end he was overthrown and his religion cast aside.

What we may perhaps call "celestial religion" reached its peak with Akhenaten, since, for a few years, the greatest civilization of the time changed over to solar worship, with the Sun as the only god. Strictly speaking, it should be added that the change was official only; many of the Pharaoh's subjects did not approve of it, and the established priesthood certainly did not, which is why it failed

28

to take root. Yet it was immensely significant, and
had Akhenaten's revolution been successful it
might easily have changed the whole course of world
history.

Of course, the Egyptians were not the first people
to worship the Sun, the Moon or other bodies in the
sky. No doubt the Ice Age hunters did so. Nothing
could be more natural, particularly with the Sun,
which is so obviously the giver of all light and heat,
and without which we could not exist. The Moon,
too, plays its part during the hours of night, and in
the remote period before settlements and villages
came into existence the dark, moonless nights were
ideally suited to raids and plundering expeditions,
so that the Moon provided a measure of safety and
was presumably benevolent. But when considering
sky-worship, there are several important things to
be borne in mind.

First, we must distinguish between legend and
actual worship. Most of the famous legends are
Greek, and of much later date than Akhenaten;
most people, surely, have read the tale of Perseus
and the Gorgon's Head, or the story of how the
reckless boy Phæthon was granted permission to
drive the Sun-Chariot for one day, a venture that
would have ended by destroying the Earth had not
Zeus, king of the gods, struck Phæthon down with
a thunderbolt. Legends of this kind are fascinating,
but I do not think that they are relevant here.

Secondly, there were cults in which the Sun and
other celestial bodies were regarded as gods, and
other cults in which the objects in the sky were
simply associated with gods. In Greek mythology,
Zeus was linked with the largest of the planets, but
there was no suggestion that Zeus *was* the planet.

(When the Romans became supreme, they adopted a large part of Greek mythology, and re-named the Greek gods; thus Zeus became Jupiter. Nowadays we use the Roman names, though they are not so ancient and the gods themselves are not always identical.)

Chronologically, we must start with the Sumerians, because it was they who first developed the art of writing. In their religion the sun-god Utu played an important part. So too did Nanna, the Moon, and Inanna, goddess of love, who was associated with the planet we now call Venus. Temples to these gods were set up, and during the period of Babylonian greatness it seems that Marduk, the chief god, was a solar deity who could well have been passed down by the older Sumerians.

It would be too much of a digression to go into details about the religions of the other ancient races, but generally the Sun was very much to the fore, and this was so in Egypt, where the Sun-god had many titles and many meanings. As Ra he was creator of the universe and also the first King of Egypt, so that the Pharaohs claimed descent from him and were regarded as divine in their own right. Yet Egyptian religion was not monotheistic; that is to say, it did not assume that there can be only one god. There were many gods, and Ra, in his various forms, was merely the chief of them. Among others, the name of Osiris, god of the Underworld, is particularly well remembered.

It was against this background that Akhenaten attempted his religious revolution.

Akhenaten belonged to the Eighteenth Dynasty, so that in his day the Egyptian civilization was already ancient; it had endured for well over 2,000 years, which is longer than the Christian era has lasted up to the present time. Akhenaten's father was the Pharaoh Amenophis III, and in due course the boy succeeded to the throne as Amenophis IV. Physically he was frail—he is said to have been an epileptic—and by conventional standards he was quite the wrong sort of person to assume control of a huge and turbulent nation, mainly because he was strongly opposed to the use of force, and refused to wage wars even when it would have been politically wise to do so. In the sixth year of his reign he broke with the official priesthood, and announced that he meant to found a new city, to serve as his capital and also to be the centre of the new monotheistic religion of Sun-worship.

The remarkable thing about the whole episode is not that Akhenaten failed in the end—this was inevitable—but that he should have been able to make even a beginning. His new city was actually founded, and the new religion became official, though, as we have noted, its acceptance by the people was probably due more to lip-service than to sincerity. Love and happiness were the key-notes of the whole cult, and cruelty was abhorrent. Akhenaten knew nothing about machine-guns, poison gas or nuclear weapons; but if any of these had been available to him we can hardly imagine that he would have used them under any circumstances.

It is easy to dismiss Akhenaten as a starry-eyed idealist. This he may well have been, but at least he was honest, and he practised what he preached. When he was overthrown, in some manner unknown to us, his city was abandoned, and the priesthood did its best to wipe out all traces of his religion. Within a few years, nothing remained.

So far as we know, nothing on the scale of Akhenaten's experiment has ever been tried in the world before or since. What would have happened if his ideals had taken hold, and had been adopted permanently? Historians will say that Egypt would have crumbled away as a great power, and this is probably true; the military situation was already becoming serious before Akhenaten was deposed. The counter-argument to this is to point out that Egyptian power decayed in any case, so that it did not make much difference in the long run. And if the Egyptians had kept to Akhenaten's "religion of love", it is permissible to suggest that they might have made a greater contribution to humanity than they actually did.

Let us now pass over several centuries, and come back to the Greeks, whose whole outlook was so very different from that of Akhenaten, or indeed of any Egyptian. With Ancient Greece we find a highly-developed religion, and there were numerous gods, headed by Zeus. Though each planet was linked with a deity, the Greeks knew quite well that the planets are other worlds, even if subordinate to Earth. Science and religion were starting to separate, and astronomy was more or less divorced from Olympus.

This is not to suggest that the Greek outlook was truly modern. It was nothing of the sort, as we can see by making even a brief study of the views expressed by Plato, whose contributions to astronomy were relatively minor compared with his general philosophy, but who is justly regarded as one of the greatest thinkers of the Classical period. Plato was born in 429 B.C., and had a somewhat chequered career. This was the time of the disastrous war between the two most powerful Greek city-states, Athens and Sparta, which eventually ruined both, and led to the eclipse of Greece as a major power. In the war itself, Athens was the loser, and never again rose to its former pre-eminence. Plato was an Athenian, though for many years he travelled as far afield as Egypt and Sicily before coming back to his homeland to found an Academy of learning just outside the city.

Plato's writings on morals, politics, education, law and other subjects do not concern us here, but his views about the universe are highly relevant. Each body in the sky has a soul, while the universe itself is divine, intelligent and eternal. One short quotation, from his *Epinomis*, is revealing. He says: "It is not possible that the Earth and the heaven, the stars and the masses as a whole which they comprise should, if they have no soul attached to each body or dwelling in each body, nevertheless accurately describe their paths in the sky as they do, year by year, month by month, and day by day, and that all of us should receive all the blessings which actually come to us." This may seem a backward step from Anaxagoras' picture of the Sun as a red-hot stone, and certainly Plato was not primarily an astronomer, but his teachings carried great weight.

Sky-worship continued long after Plato, and even long after Ptolemy, with whose death the ancient period of astronomy came to a virtual end. Much more recently there have been the Aztecs of Mexico, with their ferocious Sun-God to whom countless victims were sacrificed; there were, too, the Incas of Peru, who claimed to be Children of the Sun, and whose temple in their capital, Cuzco, contained an image of the Sun made in solid gold, so placed that when the temple doors were opened at dawn the first rays of the rising Sun fell upon the image. No doubt there are still some primitive peoples who look to the sky to see their gods. But sky-worship of the old kind belongs to the past so far as the great nations are concerned, and we have come a long way in pure knowledge since the time of Akhenaten, even though our ideals fall so far short of his.

Signs in the Sky

OVER FOUR THOUSAND years ago, well before Akhenaten's time, an emperor named Chung K'ang ascended the throne of China. He was the fourth Emperor of the Hsia Dynasty, and he may well

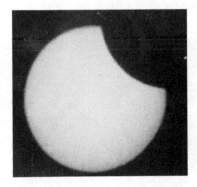

A partial eclipse of the Sun, showing the "bite", as seen from Armagh on 20 May 1966

have been an enlightened ruler; but he would hardly have been remembered in history but for a strange event that is said to have taken place in 2136 B.C., during his reign.

It was a well-known fact among the ancient Chinese that the Sun, giver of all light and heat, is occasionally threatened by dragons. These dragons can even be seen trying to eat the Sun, and the only way to scare them off is to shoot arrows at them, shout at them, beat drums, hammer upon gongs, and in general create the maximum

35

amount of noise. Fortunately the attacks by dragons can be predicted, and this gives ample time for preparations to be made.

The Imperial Court of 2136 B.C. was therefore most alarmed to find that the dragon was in action at the wrong moment. The chief astronomers of the Empire, Hsi and Ho, had given no indication that an attack was due, and yet the Sun was changing from a brilliant disk into a crescent. There was widespread consternation, followed by relief when the crisis passed and the Sun returned to normal, with the dragon presumably frightened back into the infernal region from which dragons come.

The sad ending to the tale is that Hsi and Ho were seized, tried and executed on the grounds of incompetence. It was thought that they had exposed

An eclipse of the Moon, as seen from Hertfordshire on 4 May 1966

their land to the anger of Heaven, and were thus deserving of death.

Looking at the episode now, it is quite clear that the cause of the phenomenon was a solar eclipse. At such times the Moon passes in between the Sun and the Earth, and it really does seem as though the Sun is being "bitten". If the eclipse is total, the sky becomes dark, and the Sun's atmosphere, known to us as the corona, flashes into view; the sight is truly wonderful, and nobody who has seen a total solar eclipse is ever likely to forget it.

The Chinese of ancient times had no idea that the Moon is concerned in eclipses, but they did know how to make rough predictions. If the Moon's path round the Earth lay in exactly the plane of the Earth's orbit round the Sun, there would be a solar eclipse at every new moon. However, the true situation is rather different. The lunar orbit is tilted by rather more than 5 degrees, and at most new moons there is no eclipse; the Moon, with its dark side toward us, passes either above or below the Sun in the sky, and so does not betray its presence. For an eclipse to occur, new moon must occur when the Moon is very close to a "node", i.e. the point where the lunar orbit crosses the plane of the ecliptic. For various reasons which need not concern us here, the Sun, Moon and node return to almost the same relative positions after a period of 6,585 days 8 hours, or rather over 18 years, a period that has become known as the Saros. Eclipses can therefore be forecast by simple addition, since any particular eclipse will be followed by another one 6,585 days 8 hours later.

The Saros cycle is not exact, and eclipses of the Sun do not recur identically. Thus the eclipse of

1927 was total over some parts of England, but the "return", in 1945, was not. All the same, the Saros method is much better than nothing at all, and the Chinese made regular use of it.

There are several versions of the Hsi and Ho legend. According to one of them, the luckless astronomers were drunk, and were executed not because they failed to predict the eclipse, but because they were in no fit state to carry out their duties during the dragon's attack. Personally, I have the gravest doubts as to whether the story has any truth in it, but it is by no means impossible, and it serves to show that the Chinese were close observers of eclipses. Historians as well as scientists have found the old eclipse records very useful indeed.[1]

Perhaps I may be allowed to digress briefly in order to give one example of the value of ancient eclipse observations. As the Moon travels round the Earth (or, properly speaking, round the gravitational centre of the Earth-Moon system) it tends to slow down the Earth's spin on its axis. Our rotation period is increasing by 0·00000002 seconds every day, so that on an average, neglecting shorter-term fluctuations, each day is 0·00000002 seconds longer than its predecessor. This may not seem very much, but over the centuries it adds up, and it is found that the very old eclipse records betray it. When we

---

[1] I cannot resist quoting a piece of doggerel, which runs:
> Here lie the bodies of Hsi and Ho,
> Whose fate, though sad, was visible:
> Being slain because they could not spy
> Th'eclipse which was invisible.

I am not sure of the author's identity, but I hardly think that he was resident in Ancient China!

check the calculated eclipse times against the
Chinese records, the effect of the lengthening of the
day, known technically as "secular acceleration",
is quite obvious.

The Moon can also suffer eclipse, but in a rather
different manner. Since it is closer to the Earth than
any other natural body in the sky, there is nothing
capable of passing between it and the Earth. A lunar
eclipse is caused when
the Moon passes into the
Earth's shadow; its sup-
ply of sunlight is cut off,
and it turns a dim, often
coppery colour until it
comes out of the shadow
again. The first recorded
lunar eclipse goes back
to the 35th year of Wen-
Wang, on the day of Ping-
Tzu—or, more familiarly,

The 1954 total eclipse of the
Sun, as seen from Sweden.
Note the bright prominence
at the Sun's limb

2 January, 1136 B.C.
Eclipses of the Moon, like
those of the Sun, obey
the Saros law, and so
they too could be forecast. No doubt this was done
not only by the Chinese, but also by the Sumerians
and other early star-gazers.

The Greeks had no faith in dragons, and attempted
to explain the eclipses in a scientific manner.
Xenophanes, who was contemporary with Pythagoras and is said to have lived to the age of one
hundred, wrote that "there are many suns and
moons according to the regions, divisions and zones
of the Earth; at certain times, the disk falls on some
division of the Earth not inhabited by us, and thus

when, as it were, stepping where there is void, exhibits eclipse''.

Xenophanes' theories may be less fanciful than those of the Chinese, but one has to admit that they are not much more logical. Of course, he could not be expected to hit upon the truth, because, unlike Pythagoras, he did not believe the Earth to be a globe. Yet all the Greek philosophers, from Thales onward, were able to predict eclipses by the Saros method, and Thales himself was responsible for the first prediction of which we have definite historical knowledge. He seems to have announced that an eclipse would take place on 28 May, 585 B.C. He was correct—and in dramatic fashion, since the eclipse put an abrupt end to a battle between the armies of two nations of Asia Minor, the Lydians and the Medes. To quote Herodotus: "Just as the battle was growing warm, day was suddenly changed into night. When the Lydians and the Medes observed the change, they ceased fighting, and were anxious to conclude peace." The Lydians, at least, worshipped the Sun and Moon, so that they may well have regarded the strange darkening of the sky as a sign of divine displeasure.

But if the eclipse of 585 B.C. brought peace to the Lydians, the eclipse of 413 B.C. brought nothing but disaster to the great city-state of Athens, and it is not too much to say that the timing of the eclipse altered world history. This was the time of the Peloponnesian War between Athens, the centre of learning and oratory, and Sparta, the military state in which power and conquest were all-important. Rather unwisely, the Athenians had dispatched an army to the island of Sicily, and had met with reverse after reverse. The only logical course was to withdraw, but unfortunately the Athenian commander, Nicias, delayed evacuation of the island because of an eclipse, which he interpreted as being divine advice to stay where he was. By the time he did make up his mind to embark, it was too late. Gylippus, the Spartan leader, launched an attack, and of all the Athenian thousands only a scattered few survived to return home years later; Nicias himself was among the victims.

The Sicilian disaster proved to be the turning-point of the war, and within ten years Athens had surrendered. Sparta was no substitute as the leader of the Greek city-states, and from that time onward the fortunes of true Greece went downhill. So far as the eclipse was concerned, the most surprising part of the whole affair is that Nicias paid any attention to it. At least fifty years earlier, Anaxagoras had explained the causes of eclipses quite correctly, and Nicias, as one of the chief men of Athens, should surely have known. The fact that he did not know was tragic both for his people and for himself.

It is something of a coincidence that another eclipse in the region of Sicily, more than a century later, was also associated with a sea-battle. It happened during the August of 310 B.C., at the time of a struggle in Sicily between the Greeks and the Carthaginians. Agathocles, Tyrant of Syracuse, was the Greek commander; he had managed to slip his fleet out of Syracuse under cover of darkness, and was being chased by the Carthaginian ships when a total eclipse of the Sun caused consternation among his pursuers. Agathocles, wiser than Nicias, made the most of his opportunity, and was even able to effect a landing in Africa and do a great deal of damage to the Carthaginian territories.

By then, of course, astronomy was making real progress, and eclipses were fully understood, but a total eclipse of the Sun was still apt to cause alarm and despondency among the mass of the people. This was still true long after the end of Greek power, and it is worth pausing to note a proclamation made by the Roman emperor Claudius in A.D. 45.

Claudius was an extraordinary man. According to some historians, he was weak-minded, and entirely at the mercy of his advisers; according to others, he was brilliantly clever, but preferred not to show it. Since he had a long and highly successful reign, according to the standards of the period, the latter view seems much the more likely. (Incidentally, it was Claudius who conquered Britain—not Julius Cæsar, whose two earlier raids had been somewhat abortive.)

Claudius was a good scholar, and seems to have had a sound knowledge of science as well. The eclipse of A.D. 45 happened to coincide with his birthday, and he thought that there might be general uneasiness, so he issued a statement which not only gave an accurate prediction of what was to happen but also explained the reasons for it. Actually, the eclipse was not total in Rome; barely half the Sun was covered.

Also, we must note the eclipse of A.D. 840, which is said to have frightened the Emperor Louis of Bavaria so much that he died of terror—after which his sons proceeded to fight over the succession, so hastening the break-up of the great empire which had been founded by Charlemagne. Later eclipses, too, have caused panic. In 1544 the historian Leovitius announced that the eclipse of that year would cause pestilence, wars and famine, and a great many people believed him. But such forecasts were mainly astrological, and by the sixteenth century most people were inclined to discount them.

Christopher Columbus once turned an eclipse of the Moon to good account. During his stay in Jamaica, the local natives refused to supply him with food, and supplies were running short when Columbus remembered that a lunar eclipse was due. He told the un-cooperative tribesmen that unless they granted his request, he would make the Moon "change her colour and lose her light". The eclipse took place on schedule, and the results, so far as Columbus was concerned, were gratifying, since the Jamaicans were so alarmed that they provided all the supplies that were needed.

However, eclipses never caused the widespread terror associated with comets. Nowadays we know that comets are among the most unsubstantial of all the bodies in the sky; even a brilliant comet is made up merely of small particles and extremely thin gas, while the long, impressive tail could do no harm even if the Earth passed right through it (as has, in fact, happened more than once during the past few centuries). Needless to say, the Chinese kept records of comets, and there is, too, a reference in the poems of Homer, that somewhat mysterious bard to whom are attributed the *Iliad* and the *Odyssey*. During the account of the war between the Greeks and the Trojans, we find the lines

> Like the red star, that from his flaming hair
> Shakes down diseases, pestilence and war.

This is a definite reference to a comet. We do not know which comet was meant, and it is not even

certain that Homer may be regarded as an historical
figure, but the allusion is unmistakable, and it is
certainly very ancient.

The Chinese, on the other hand, were not so
apprehensive. They believed that each Earthly
kingdom has its celestial counterpart, and that the
comets move like ambassadors from one region to
another. The idea of a comet as "a blazing star,
supposed to portend destruction to kings and
princes" (to quote the Roman writer Suetonius)
seems to be more recent, though it may have been
prevalent even at the time of the Trojan War.

Curiously, the fear of comets seems to have grown
with the passing of time. Pliny, who was killed
during the eruption of Vesuvius in A.D. 79, recorded
that "we have in the war between Cæsar and
Pompey an example of the terrible effects which
follow the apparition of a comet . . . that fearsome
star which overthrows the powers of the Earth,
showing its terrible locks". Shortly after Cæsar's
murder, in 43 B.C., another comet was seen, apparently carrying away his soul. This was referred
to, centuries later, by Shakespeare:

> When beggars die, there are no comets seen;
> The heavens themselves blaze forth the death of princes.

In A.D. 79, the year of the Vesuvius eruption which
destroyed Pompeii and Herculaneum (and which
killed Pliny), another comet was seen. Almost at
at the same time the death occurred of another
famous man—Vespasian, who had reigned as Emperor of Rome for the previous nine years. Vespasian
was one of the better Emperors, blessed with abundant common-sense, but he was not unaffected by
mysticism and astrology, accentuated by a visit to

Comet Ikeya-Seki, seen from Valparaiso on 3 November 1965

the astrology-ridden country of Egypt. When he was dying, and his courtiers told him that a comet had become visible, his dry comment was: "This hairy star does not concern me. It menaces rather the King of the Parthians, for he is hairy, while I am bald."

Vespasian was not the only Emperor to die during the visibility of a bright comet. Another was Macrinus, whose death occured in A.D. 218, when a comet was seen in Rome and likened to "a fearful, flaming star". Macrinus, however, was no Vespasian: he was merely one of the succession of nonentities who occupied the Imperial throne during the period following the death of the philosopher-emperor Marcus Aurelius.

We know a great deal about the comet of A.D. 218. It was Halley's Comet, which becomes visible every

76 years. Edmond Halley, the second Astronomer Royal of England, observed a comet in 1682, and worked out its orbit, finding, rather to his surprise, that the path seemed to be almost identical with those of comets previously seen in 1607 and 1531. Halley came to the conclusion that the three comets were one and the same, and that it would return once more in 1758. Though he himself was dead by then, the comet duly returned, and was named in his honour. Since then it has been seen at two more returns, those of 1835 and 1910, and is due back again in 1986. At the moment it is too far-off and too faint to be observed, though we know where it must be.

Halley's Comet has been tracked back into Classical times, and was observed by Anaxagoras as long ago as 467 B.C. There are later historical associations also; the comet reappeared in 1066, when Harold Godwinson ruled England, and Duke William of Normandy was preparing his great invasion. The comet was thought by the Saxons to be a bad omen, and it was addressed by one of the monks of Malmesbury in the following words: "I see you then, origin of the tears of many mothers; I have seen you for long, but now you appear more terrible, since you threaten my country with entire ruin." The scene has been recorded for us in a panel of the famous Bayeux Tapestry, said by some authorities to have been woven by the Conqueror's wife. A messenger is announcing the arrival of the comet, and Harold is so overcome that he totters on his throne.

The fear of comets was slow to die, and still lingers on in some countries. I cannot resist quoting the proclamation issued by the Town Council at Baden, in Switzerland, when a comet with "a frightful long tail" was seen over Europe in 1681. The Council ordered that "all are to attend Mass and Sermon every Sunday and Feast Day, not leaving the church before the sermon or staying away without good reason; all must abstain from playing or dancing, whether at weddings or on other occasions; none must wear unseemly clothing, nor swear nor curse".

End-of-the-world panics have been caused by comets, and of particular note was the episode of 1773, when terror swept over France. It was suggested that the comet might hit the Earth, and cause widespread damage or even total destruction. Enterprising businessmen took advantage of the situation, and it is said that seats in Paradise were sold at a high price! Also, there was the prophecy of William Miller, who fixed the date of the end of the world at 21 March 1843. Miller made his prediction by mathematical calculations based on the writings in the Bible, and was supremely confident of himself, so that when a great comet made its appearance, in February, thousands of people joined him in prayer to await the end. It is true that the comet of 1843 was one of the most brilliant on record, but it never came anywhere near the Earth—and it would have caused nothing more than local damage even if it had scored a direct hit.

Nobody is quite sure of the size of the nucleus of a comet. Certainly it must be large enough to devastate a wide area if it happened to collide, and there are suggestions that the so-called Siberian "Meteorite" of 1908, which blew pine-trees flat for miles all round the point of impact, was in fact the nucleus of a comet. But the risk of another collision of this kind is very slight indeed, and so far as the mediæval comet-panics were concerned it seems that the main fears were intangible.

I have digressed somewhat from the theme of "signs in the sky", but it seemed worth following the eclipse and comet fears through to relatively modern times, and it only remains to add that in 1910, during the appearance of a bright comet (the Daylight Comet, not identical with Halley's) one manufacturing firm made a considerable sum of money by selling what were called comet pills. It is not clear just what these pills were meant to do, and they were no more valid than the tablets sold in the American town of Dallas on Friday 13 August 1954, as "woofus pills", or anti-Friday the Thirteenth potions. . . . The vendor in this case was apprehended by the local police, though I have never been able to find out what happened to him.

Among the "signs" regarded with awe and uneasiness in ancient times were the aurorae or polar lights, which are not often to be seen in low latitudes, but are very common in the Arctic and Antarctic regions; even in North Scotland they are frequently on view, and they may make occasional spectacular displays over much of Europe.

In Rome, aurorae are rare enough to cause widespread interest, so that it is natural for them to have been regarded as ominous in Classical times. According to the historian Livy, there was a major display in 464 B.C., when "the heavens were seen to blaze with numerous fires, and other portents were either actually seen or were due to the illusions of the terror-stricken observers. To avert these alarms, a three-days' session of prayer was ordered".

However, Livy was writing of events which had happened five hundred years before his own time, and for the earliest eye-witness descriptions of aurorae we must turn to Aristotle, who, as usual,

An aurora, seen from Northumberland on 4 December 1958

does not fail us. He wrote: "Sometimes on a fine night, we see a variety of appearances that form in the sky; chasms, for instances, and trenches, and blood-red colours." He probably witnessed the display of 349 B.C., described by an unknown writer as "something that looks like blood, and a fire that falls from it to Earth—the most alarming possible cause of terror to mankind".

The reference to blood is quite understandable, because auroræ are often of a strongly red colour. This caused a minor panic in Rome in A.D. 20, when the whole sky was seen to glow. The Emperor Tiberius was convinced that the port of Ostia must be burning, and ordered out his fire-fighting squads, who were presumably somewhat puzzled when they arrived at the port to find no blaze.

Like comets, auroræ were regarded as signs of ill fortune, and this idea still lingers on in parts of North Scotland, where the Lights are known as "the Merry Dancers". And looking back to 12 January 1570, we find a description of an aurora which was so bright that "no such gruesome spectacle had been seen or heard of within living memory". The writer went on: "Wherefore, dear Christians, take such terrible portents to heart and diligently pray to God, that he will soften his punishments and bring us back into his favour."

Auroræ occur in the upper part of the Earth's atmosphere, but their cause lies in the Sun. Streams of electrified particles sent out by the Sun strike the top part of the Earth's atmosphere, and make it glow; because the particles are charged, they are naturally attracted to the magnetic poles, which is why auroræ are best seen from high latitudes. The process is not so straightforward as used to be thought before the beginning of the Space Age, and we now know that the radiation zone surrounding the Earth, known as the Van Allen Zone in honour of its discoverer, is closely involved. But the Van Allen Zone was not detected until 1958, and in ancient times there was no thought of linking auroræ with events on the Sun. Indeed, it would have been heretical to suggest that the Sun could be anything but a pure, unmarked disk—even though naked-eye sunspots are seen sometimes, and the Chinese, in particular, had recorded quite a number of them.

Of all signs in the sky, the most famous is, of course, the Star of Bethlehem. Let us admit that our information is scanty from the outset; the only reference to the Star is in the Bible, in Chapter 2 of the Gospel according to St. Matthew, and all we are really told is that the star was seen in the east, and "went before" the Three Wise Men. There are no astronomical records of any unusual event at that time, and moreover we are very uncertain about our dates. Our "A.D." dates are reckoned according to the calculations of a Roman monk who died in the year we call A.D. 556, and it seems certain that Christ was born several years earlier than the year known to us as A.D. 1. December 25th was not celebrated as Christmas Day until the fourth century— by which time the real date had been forgotten, so that our Christmas is wrong too. It is a decidedly unpromising start to any efforts we may make to learn more about the Star of Bethlehem.

Of one thing we may be sure: the Star was not Venus, Jupiter or any other planet. If it were really seen, it must have been unusual, and all the familiar bodies in the sky can be rejected out of hand. Neither was the Star due to a conjunction of two planets— that is to say, to two planets lying so close together in the sky that with the naked eye they would show up as one exceptionally brilliant point. Such conjunctions do occur sometimes, but there was nothing suitable within the time-limits that we can set for the Star of Bethlehem.

It is just possible that the Star was nothing more nor less than Halley's Comet, which returned to perihelion in 11 B.C. and is therefore just about within our time-range even though most theologians believe that the most likely date for Christ's birth is 4 B.C. Another possibility is a nova, which is simply a faint star which suffers a tremendous outburst and flares up to brilliance for a few days, weeks or months before sinking back to its former obscurity. On the other hand, a bright nova would presumably have been recorded by the astronomers of the day—which it was not.

My own tentative suggestion is that if we regard the Star of Bethlehem as anything more than a myth, the best explanation is that it may have been due to two meteors, seen at different times in much the same direction, and moving eastwards. But it is really rather pointless to speculate, because our only guide, St. Matthew, simply does not give enough material for a proper discussion.

I have dwelt at some length upon the various "signs in the sky" because they are important in any evaluation of Man's changing views of the universe. In the remote past, everything in the sky was mysterious and unattainable; this was so for the Chinese, the Egyptians and the earlier Greeks. Then, with the genius of the Greek philosophers, the movements of the bodies in the sky were studied, and some of the phenomena formerly described as divine were explained quite easily, eclipses being the obvious case in point. By the end of the Classical period, mysticism had more or less given way to science, and at the end of mediæval times it was only the uninformed who were terrified by ominous-looking signs such as comets. This was a major step forward. Yet there was still one influence which had to be eliminated before there could be any real understanding. This was the dead hand of astrology.

[5]

The Astrologers

BEFORE THE NATURE of the universe came to be understood, it was not absurd to think that the celestial bodies might have an effect upon men's destinies. This almost certainly accounts for the rise of astrology, which used to be classed as a genuine science. It is not dead even yet; it is still widely practised in some Asian countries (India in particular), and it survives in Europe, though only the gullible take it seriously.

Nowadays, the word "astrology" is associated with certain Sunday newspapers, which print columns upon "what the stars foretell" and set out to predict the events of the coming week. Less is heard of the astrological societies, which, like the Flat Earthers, take themselves very seriously indeed, and even issue "degrees" to people who are ready to pay a fee for a course of instruction! But in ancient times there was no official distinction between astrology and astronomy. Probably the first writer to distinguish between the two in unmistakable terms was Isidorus, Bishop of Seville, about A.D. 570.

Basically, astrology is the superstition of the sky.

The most important bodies are taken to be the Sun, Moon and planets, each of which has its own particular influence; Saturn, for instance, is generally baleful, while Jupiter is benign. Moreover, each planet is said to be associated with a particular part of the human body. The Egyptians allotted the left eye to Saturn, the tongue to Mercury, the right nostril to Mars, and so on.

The power and effect of a planet is—so we are told —dependent upon its position in the sky, and this brings us on to horoscopes, which are charts of the planetary positions. To cast a horoscope, an astrologer (ancient or modern) looks up the exact positions of the planets at the time of the subject's birth, plots them on a complicated and imposing-looking diagram, and then draws conclusions as to the character, temperament and destiny of the person concerned. A few hours' difference in the subject's time of birth will mean, of course, that the astrological pattern will work out quite differently.

In the Solar System there are five planets which are visible to the naked eye, and which were already known when written history began. All of them— Mercury, Venus, Mars, Jupiter and Saturn—move round the Sun in roughly the same plane, since the angle of inclination to the plane of the Earth's orbit is a mere 7 degrees for Mercury and less than 4 degrees for all the rest. A moment's thought will show that for this reason the planets will be seen only in certain areas of the sky, and will be confined to a definite belt, known as the Zodiac. This also applies to the Sun and Moon, and to the other large planets (Uranus and Neptune) discovered in modern times.

Originally the Zodiac was studied by the Greeks,

and was divided up into twelve constellations:
Aries (the Ram), Taurus (the Bull), Gemini (the
Twins), Cancer (the Crab), Leo (the Lion), Virgo
(the Virgin), Libra (the Scales or Balance; origin-
ally the Scorpion's Claws), Scorpio (the Scorpion),
Sagittarius (the Archer), Capricornus (the Sea-
Goat), Aquarius (the Water-bearer) and Pisces (the
Fishes). These twelve groups were listed by Ptolemy,

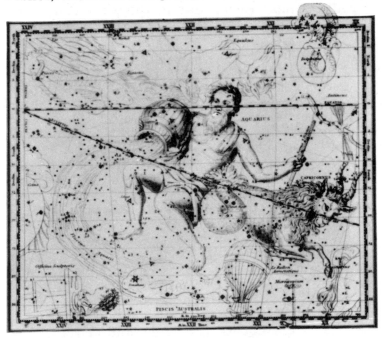

The constellation figure Aquarius, the Water-Bearer, from
an old woodcut

and we still use them, though in some cases the out-
lines have been modified. Our modern star-maps

still contain all Ptolemy's total of 48 constellations, though many have been altered and new
groups have been added. Of the constellations in
the Zodiac, some are prominent while others are
obscure, but astrologers regard them as of equal
importance.

Aries was taken as the first constellation of the
Zodiac, because it contained what is known as the
Vernal Equinox. Every March, about the 21st of the
month, the Sun crosses the equator of the sky,
moving from south to north. This marks the beginning of northern spring, and the Sun remains north
of the celestial equator until the following Sep-
tember. The Vernal Equinox is the point at which
the Sun crosses the equator in March; it is still
known commonly as the First Point of Aries, but it
is not marked by any bright star, and is no longer in
Aries. The effects of precession have caused a shift
in the position of the celestial equator, and the
First Point has been moved into the neighbouring
constellation of Pisces.

The Moon and planets are seen against the background of the stars, and seem to form part of the
general pattern. As I write these words (in 1968),
Saturn, for instance, lies in Pisces, but by 1969 it
will have crawled into Aries, and by 1971 it will
have reached Taurus; in time it will work its way
all round the Zodiac, and begin another circuit.
The other planets behave in similar fashion, though
their rates are not all the same, and Mercury and
Venus, which are closer to the Sun than we are,
have apparent motions of rather different type. As
we have noted, the stars appear to keep fixed in
their relative positions, while the planets move
about. This was certainly how early peoples were

able to tell the difference between the planets and the stars.

Actually, the stars are not fixed in space. They are moving about in all sorts of directions at all sorts of speeds, and they seem to stand still only because they are so remote for us. The planets, which are our near neighbours, wander quite obviously even from one week to the next.

Now let us go back to the astrologer's horoscope. He works out (or, more probably, looks up) the planetary positions, and claims that because certain planets are in certain constellations they will have various definite effects. Everything, in fact, depends upon which Zodiacal groups the planets happen to be in.

Unfortunately for this rather curious idea, a constellation is not a connected unit; it is a mere line of sight effect, and the stars in any particular constellation are not truly associated with each other. Consider Leo (the Lion), one of the most striking of the Zodiacal groups, which dominates the southern part of the sky during spring evenings and which is recognizable at a glance. Regulus, the brightest star in the constellation, seems reasonably close to Denebola, as shown in the diagram, so that both are included in the Leo pattern. Yet Regulus is twice as remote from us as Denebola; it simply happens to lie in much the same direction as seen from Earth. In fact, Regulus is just as far away from Denebola as we are.

In the diagram, I have also added the position of the planet Jupiter for mid-1968. It, too, was then said to be in Leo. But it is nothing of the kind; it is very much closer to us. Some sort of analogy can be drawn by holding, say, a pencil at arm's-length

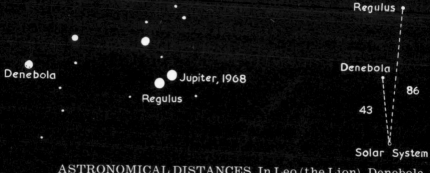

ASTRONOMICAL DISTANCES. In Leo (the Lion), Denebola is 43 light-years from us, and Regulus 86; therefore, Regulus is as remote from Denebola as we are, and seems to be "in" the same constellation only because it happens to lie in roughly the same direction as seen from Earth. This is shown in the right-hand diagram. In 1968, the planet Jupiter also lay "in" Leo, but of course Jupiter, as a member of the Solar System, is very much closer to us and has no connection whatsoever with any of the stars "in" Leo

and lining it up with a distant clump of trees. It would not seem very logical to claim that the pencil is then "in the trees", but this is just as sensible as saying that during 1968 Jupiter was "in Leo".

Astrologers are also deeply concerned with the Zodiacal constellations themselves, each of which plays a part; thus Pisces is a watery sign. This is another piece of weird and wonderful reasoning, because Pisces, taken as a typical example, is made up of a line of stars, and looks nothing like the outline of a pair of fishes; it was named by the ancients, but for no obvious reason, and to associate it with a watery influence is totally absurd. Also, the fact that the planets may enter other constellations as well as the official twelve is tacitly ignored. Ophiuchus, the Serpent-bearer, intrudes into the Zodiac for some distance between Scorpio and Sagittarius, while during part of 1968 Saturn passed into Cetus (the Whale), though admittedly it was very close to the boundary of Pisces. Pluto, the outermost of the known planets, has a much greater orbital tilt, and may leave the Zodiac altogether, though it is a very slow mover; it was discovered only in 1930, so that the ancients knew nothing about it. For that matter, Uranus, discovered in 1781, and Neptune, first detected in 1846, were equally unknown during the heyday of astrology, but seem to have found no difficulty in fitting themselves into the modern scheme.

All ancient astronomers were also astrologers, and the mixture of true and false continued for many centuries after Ptolemy's time. In a way, it was surprisingly beneficial. Following the end of Greek brilliance, there came the so-called Dark Ages in Europe, when science was to all intents and purposes at a standstill. When the revival came, it was due largely to the Arabs, and had an astrological slant. Men wanted to learn their destinies, and for horoscope-casting a certain knowledge of the positions of the stars and the movements of the planets was needed. For this reason, observation was re-started; early in the 9th century A.D., Al Mamun, Caliph of Baghdad, established an observatory, and the Arab school of astronomy-cum-astrology flourished for several centuries. Ironically, its end was also linked with astrology. Ulugh Beigh, grandson of the Oriental conqueror Tamerlane, had set up an observatory at his capital in Samarkand; he prepared tables of the movements of the planets, drew up a catalogue of over a thousand stars which was quite independent of Ptolemy's, and even established an Academy of Science. Unfortunately he cast the horoscope of his eldest son, Abdallatif, and found to his alarm that the boy was destined to kill him. Prudently, he dismissed Abdallatif from

Court, stripped him of his honours, and nominated a younger son as heir in his stead. Abdallatif was not to be set aside so lightly. He rebelled, attacked his father's capital, and had Ulugh Beigh murdered. Certainly this was one astrological prediction which came true—but it also ended the great period of Arab science.

It is not easy nowadays to realize the immense power wielded by astrologers not so very many centuries ago. They were consulted on all important matters, and their advice was generally followed. Now and then they caused widespread panics. One of these was sparked off in 1524 by Johann Stoeffler, in Germany, who forecast a great flood which would result in the destruction of mankind. Stoeffler, one of the best-known astrologers of his day, had found (quite correctly) that in February 1524 several planets would lie close together in the sky, in the constellation of Pisces; this, he announced, could only mean that there would be devastation by water. In the resulting terror, dozens of people were killed, and the effects spread from Germany across much of Europe, though England remained unmoved. Rulers and statesmen were affected, and in particular President Auriol of Toulouse University spent weeks in building a sort of ark, though when the flood failed to materialize he took care to explain that he had really meant it for fishing. The Elector of Brandenburg collected all his portable possessions and set out for a nearby mountain-top, where he remained for some time, much too frightened to come down. Even so, Stoeffler's high reputation was not damaged, and he remained famous and respected until his death seven years later.

Among other horoscope-casters were Tycho Brahe,

Tycho Brahe, observer and astrologer, from a woodcut

the eccentric Dane who drew up the best star-catalogue of pre-telescopic times, and Johann Kepler, who first proved beyond doubt that the Earth moves round the Sun instead of vice versa. The Rev. John Flamsteed, first Astronomer Royal, went so far as to cast a horoscope for Greenwich Observatory, which was founded in 1675 by order of King Charles II—but it does not seem that Flamsteed treated the horoscope very seriously, since he ended it with the words "Risum teneatis, amici?" (Can you help laughing, my friends?). Sir Isaac Newton, often regarded as the greatest scientist of all time, was something of a mystic, and was not unsympathetic to astrology even though he did not openly practise it.

It is difficult to say just when astrology ceased to be accepted as a genuine science. It was still strong in 1700, and moderately popular in 1800, though it was certainly discredited well before the end of the nineteenth century. Its worst effect was that for a long time it held back the progress of true astronomy, since consistent efforts were made to adapt scientific theories to the needs of astrological

Greenwich Observatory in 1675, when the Rev. John Flamsteed cast a horoscope for it

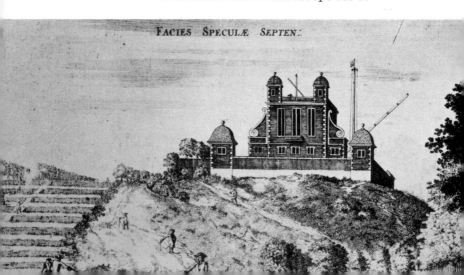

FACIES SPECULÆ SEPTEN:

creed. Of course, this sort of thing belongs to the past; but it did occur, and it acted as a very effective brake.

The modern cult of astrology is confined strictly to the credulous. (One must note, in passing, a psychologist named C. G. Jung, who died only in 1961, and who is said to have employed an astrologer on his staff!) Actually, the cult is fairly harmless on the whole, though there have been unfortunate cases of people who have made decisions according to astrological advice and have subsequently regretted it.

Let it be made clear, at once, that many of the modern practising astrologers are completely sincere and well-meaning. They genuinely believe that they have powers of prediction, and that they can be of help to others. Also, they are convinced that they are being persecuted by cynics—an attitude of mind found just as strongly among the flat-earth believers, the flying-saucer enthusiasts, the circle-squarers and others of their kind.

It is not easy to see how anyone can believe that the apparent position of a planet viewed against a background of totally unconnected stars can affect human destiny. One can only echo the famous remark made by the Duke of Wellington in a different context: "Sir—if you will believe *that*, you will believe anything." To the best of my knowledge, astrologers have never attempted to explain the basis for their beliefs, and it would indeed be hard to do so. When challenged, the professional astrologer will not argue. He will merely refer to what he calls the Ancient Teachings (the capital letters are his), and return to his charts and horoscopes. There let us leave him.

6

Man's Place in the Universe

ASTRONOMY OF THE mid-sixteenth century was of the "old" type. The Earth lay motionless in the centre of the universe, while the Sun, Moon, planets and stars moved round it at various distances at various speeds. Our world was the supreme body, and the casting of an astrological horoscope was a matter just as important as studying the behaviour of, say, a bright comet.

A hundred and fifty years later, all was changed. The Earth had been dethroned from its proud central position, and it was becoming very clear that even the Sun is of no true importance in the universe considered as a whole. The effects of gravitation had been discovered, and astrology was declining, even though it was slow to die.

We can date the beginning and the end of the revolution quite precisely. It began in 1543, with the publication of a book by the Polish cleric Copernicus, and it ended in 1687 with Sir Isaac Newton's great work the *Principia*. As a matter of fact, the change-over from old to new was more or less complete well before 1687, but Newton put the finishing touches to it.

The long delay stemmed from the fact that the Greeks had made one fundamental mistake in their scheme of the universe, since they had insisted that the Earth must be the central body. Aristarchus of Samos and a few other philosophers had dissented, but Hipparchus and Ptolemy had followed Aristotle, and for many centuries the ideas of Aristarchus were pushed very thoroughly into the background.

The reasons for keeping the central Earth were not entirely scientific, since religion and super-stition had a great deal to do with the "official" attitude. To suppose that the Earth might be a minor body was regarded as heretical, and even the Athenians, who were much more tolerant of free speech than most other ancient or mediæval peoples, were not ready to accept it. So far as we know, no Greek philosopher was put to death for astronomical heresy, but Anaxagoras was certainly banished for teaching that the Sun is a large, red-hot stone.

Of course our chief authority on ancient science is Ptolemy, and we must pause to say something more about him, because his influence was so tremendous and so long-lasting. Some modern authors have suggested that Ptolemy was nothing more than a copyist, who extracted the best parts of his pre-decessors' work and put them into his own book, but this view is completely unjustified. It is true that Ptolemy's star catalogue was based on the measures made by Hipparchus more than two centuries earlier, but Ptolemy improved the cata-logue considerably, and must have made many measures of his own. As an observer, theorist and writer he had no superiors in the Ancient World, though he may have had his equals. The more one learns about Ptolemy, the more one admires him, and he was aptly nicknamed "the Prince of Astronomers". It was remarkably lucky that even though the original of his great book has been lost, the text has come down to us by way of the Arabs; Al Mamun, Caliph of Baghdad, had it translated into Arabic during the ninth century A.D., and posterity has been duly grateful to him.

Ptolemy, brilliant thinker though he undoubtedly was, could not break free from the tradition of a central Earth, and moreover he thought that all bodies in the sky must move in perfectly circular orbits, since a circle is the "perfect" form, and nothing short of perfection can be allowed in the heavens. He even applied this principle to the sphere to which the stars are fixed, and he did not believe that the Earth is rotating. He pointed out that if the Earth were spinning, then a bird in flight, temporarily away from its resting-place, would find the ground literally whipped away from underneath it. For this and other reasons Ptolemy concluded that the star-sphere performed one complete revolution every twenty-four hours.

For the Moon and planets, difficulties arose. The Moon does not always appear the same size; its apparent diameter varies between $33\frac{1}{2}$ seconds of arc and only $29\frac{1}{2}$ seconds of arc, which is easily measurable. Since one can hardly picture a Moon which swells and shrinks, the only answer is to assume that its distance from the Earth is not always the same. Lacking telescopes, it was clearly impossible for Ptolemy to find out whether the apparent diameters of the planets varied in the same way as that of the Moon, but probably he had a shrewd suspicion that they must do so. He was an excellent mathematician, and he must have known from the outset that the idea of uniform movements in circular orbits simply did not fit the facts.

Had he been prepared to accept a central Sun, or had he been able to abandon his perfect circles, he might well have found the correct answer to the problem. In fact, he did neither. He followed a strange, complex system which is always known as the Ptolemaic, even though Ptolemy himself perfected rather than invented it. Each body moved in a small circle or epicycle, the centre of which (the deferent) itself moved round the Earth in a perfect circle. As more and more discrepancies came to light, more and more epicycles had to be added, and it also became necessary to suppose that the centres of the large circles did not coincide with the centre of the Earth's globe. The final result was incredibly involved, and, of course, hopelessly artificial.

Yet—and this is a point all too often overlooked—the Ptolemaic system worked, inasmuch as it could account for the observed movements of the Sun, Moon and planets to well within the limits of accuracy obtainable by naked-eye observations. If it could be assumed that the celestial bodies could actually travel in the way that Ptolemy thought, then everything would fit. Ptolemy knew nothing about gravitation, and his theory satisfied unconscious prejudice as well as scientific observation, so that it became acceptable to almost everybody. It remained almost unchallenged for the following thirteen and a half centuries.

By the time that astronomy was ready to move into its next stage of development, there was another serious obstacle to be faced: religion. During mediæval times the Church was all-powerful in Europe, and to question its judgement was most unwise, since heretics were punished by torture, mutilation or death. It is a strange but undeniable fact that some of the worst cruelties in the history of mankind have been committed in the name of religion. In this respect the record of Christianity is no worse than that of many other cults, but it is certainly no better, and to claim otherwise is sheer self-deception. During the period before the Spanish conquest of Mexico (from 1519), the Aztecs used to sacrifice prisoners to their Sun-God; but was this worse than the burning of Protestants in the England of Mary Tudor, over thirty years later?

Nicolaus Koppernigk, better known to us by his Latinized name of Copernicus, was born in 1473. His life was not particularly eventful. He attended the University of Krakow, studied mathematics and medicine in Rome, and then took Holy Orders, probably at the insistence of his uncle, who was a bishop. Copernicus became attached to the cathedral of Frauenberg near the mouth of the river Vistula, in his native Poland, and remained there until his death at the age of over seventy.

As a member of the Church, Copernicus was well aware of the official attitude toward heretics—and from an early stage in his career he was himself a secret heretic. He was deeply interested in astronomy, and although not a practising observer he was a far-sighted theorist. He objected to the Ptolemaic theory on the grounds that it was unnecessarily complicated, and he looked around for something better.

The first problem to be attacked was that of the stars. Did the star-sphere really turn round the Earth once a day, or could it be the Earth itself which moved? On this score, Copernicus had no doubts at all. In his own words: "Why should we hesitate to grant the Earth a motion natural and corresponding to its spherical form? And why are we not willing to acknowledge that the *appearance* of a daily rotation belongs to the heavens, its *actuality* to the Earth? The relation is similar to that of which Virgil's Æneas says: 'We sail out of the harbour, and the countries and cities recede.' " No explanation could be more straightforward. It followed, of course, that the stars need not be fixed to anything, and neither need they be at a uniform distance from us.

The Sun, Moon and planets set problems of greater complexity. It was obvious that something was badly wrong, and Copernicus removed most of the difficulties by one master-stroke. He returned to the old, long-discarded theory of Aristarchus, and placed the Sun in the centre of the Solar System, relegating the Earth to the status of an ordinary planet.

This, let us admit, was the sum total of Copernicus' achievement, and in many ways his ideas were not markedly better than Ptolemy's; he insisted upon retaining circular orbits, and he was even reduced to bringing back epicycles. Yet he had taken the vital step. The trouble was that he dared not publish it.

His book, the English title of which may be given as *Concerning the Revolutions of the Celestial Bodies*, was probably complete by 1530, but for more than a decade it remained unseen except by Copernicus' close friends and colleagues. Had it been given to the world, Copernicus would have had to face the wrath of Rome, since to suppose that the Earth did not lie in the centre of the universe would strike at the roots of Christian dogma and would weaken the political as well as the spiritual grip of the Church. Such dangerous ideas would be suppressed as violently as possible, and nobody who knew the workings of Church organization could be under any delusions as to the possible outcome. Copernicus was not prepared to run any risks, and it is hard to blame him.

Eventually he did consent to publication, but even then he took the precaution of dedicating the book to the Pope; also, his publisher added a foreword (probably without Copernicus' consent) stressing that the work was a tentative suggestion rather than a bald statement of fact. Copernicus died just about the time that the book appeared in print, so that he escaped persecution, but some of his followers were not so lucky. One, Giordano Bruno, was burned at the stake in Rome, in 1600, partly—though not entirely—because he had persistently taught the Copernican theory instead of the Ptolemaic.

Copernicus' ideas were attractive to scientists because they led to a system which was much simpler than the Ptolemaic—and generally speaking, a simple system is more likely to be correct than a scheme which involves many unprovable assumptions. As the years passed by, the Copernican theory became more and more favoured, and the Church was reduced to desperation in its efforts to check the spread of the "heresy". The Church arguments were neither scientific nor rational, but they were backed up by the full power of the Inquisition, and logical reasoning is at a marked disadvantage when faced with the instruments of the torture-chamber.

The problem was eventually cleared up in somewhat ironical fashion. Only a few months after Copernicus' death, an astronomer of very different stamp was born at Knudstrop in Denmark. His name was Tycho Brahe, and he proved to be one of the most colourful characters in the whole history of science. He was hot-tempered, cruel and almost incredibly conceited; he believed firmly in astrology; he had no patience with the Copernican heresy, and his observatory, on the Baltic island of Hven, even included a prison used to hold those of his tenants who were reluctant to pay their rents. His retinue included a dwarf, whose function was to entertain Tycho's guests (of whom there were many over the years; one visitor to Hven was King James of Scotland, afterwards James I of England). Tycho was drawn to astronomy by the appearance of a brilliant new star, which he observed in 1572 and which we now know to have been a supernova. He went so far as to write a book about it, but thought at first that it would be beneath the dignity of a Danish nobleman to lower himself to the status of a mere author, and he was persuaded to publish only after his friends had pointed out that it would be a crime to withhold his knowledge from the world. (One cannot help being reminded of Archibald Grosvenor in W. S. Gilbert's immortal *Patience!*)

Yet with all his quirks, Tycho was an observer of outstanding brilliance. He compiled a star-catalogue which was amazingly accurate in view of the fact that it was drawn up by means of naked-eye measures alone, and he also followed the movements of the planets, particularly Mars. When he died, in 1601, his observations came into the possession of his last assistant, a young German named Johann

Kepler. Kepler used them well. After years of calculation, he found that Tycho's observations of Mars could not be made to fit in with the idea of a circular orbit, either round the Earth or round the Sun; but if it were assumed that Mars moved round the Sun in an ellipse, with the Sun at one of the foci, everything fell into place. This was the death-blow to the Ptolemaic system. Kepler's Laws of Planetary Motion, two of which were published in 1609 and the third in 1618, settled the matter once and for all.

Kepler was not wholly modern in his outlook, and he was very much of a mystic. In his book *Harmonies of the World*, which contained his Third Law, he also included some strange comments about the so-called "music of the spheres"; the various planets were said to be associated with music inaudible to human ears, and performed only for the benefit of one supreme being, whose soul resided in the Sun. Also, Kepler had to cast horoscopes, since after Tycho's death he was officially employed as Imperial Mathematician to the Holy Roman Emperor, Rudolph II, who was a passionate believer in astrology and who regarded astronomy as nothing more than a necessary offshoot. And Kepler had personal troubles to face, too; at one period his mother was arrested as a witch, and Kepler had to work hard to secure her release from prison. All this seems an unusual background to an outstanding theorist, as he undoubtedly was.

Even after 1618, when the new system was on a footing so firm that it could not logically be challenged, the Church still did its best to cling to the past. Galileo, the first great telescopic astronomer, was brought before the Inquisition years later because of his teaching of the Copernican theory, and was kept under strict surveillance until his death in 1642. And some of the old books which taught that the Earth moves round the Sun were still officially outlawed by the Catholic Church as recently as 1835. My own great-grandfather must have been born around 1820; during his boyhood, had he been a Catholic, he would have been forbidden to read Copernicus. (Lest we are tempted to smile, let us bear in mind that schools in parts of the United States were forbidden to teach Darwin's theory of evolution until as lately as 1967!)

It took some decades after Kepler's revelations for the Ptolemaic theory to die. In 1651, for instance, the craters on the Moon were named by the Jesuit astronomer Riccioli, who produced a lunar map; he named each crater after a prominent scientist, and allotted the most conspicuous crater of all to Tycho, but Copernicus and Galileo were, as he put it, "flung into the Ocean of Storms", because Riccioli was no believer in the Sun-centred theory. In Russia, the old ideas persisted for longer still. The first great Russian astronomer to support the new ideas was Mikhail Lomonosov in the mid-eighteenth century.

At last there came the work of Isaac Newton, whose book the *Principia*, published in 1687, marked the final end of the Ptolemaic period. By then, too, telescopes had come into use, and astronomers were able to look further into space than ever before.

7

Telescopes and Trials

Up to the year 1609 astronomy had been chiefly of the kind we now term "positional", since it had dealt mainly with the positions and apparent movements of the bodies in the sky. There could be nothing more, because the most powerful instrument known up to that time was the human eye. Spectacles came into use rather earlier, and on rather slender evidence are said to have been invented by Roger Bacon at the end of the thirteenth century, but telescopes were unknown.

This is not to say that there were no observatories. On the contrary, establishments such as those set up by Ulugh Beigh in Samarkand or Tycho on Hven were observatories in every sense of the word. There were instruments in plenty, and the work carried out was of real accuracy. But with no optical aid, it is hopeless to attempt to see details on any of the celestial bodies apart from the Moon, where there are bright patches and dark plains which have been said to outline the famous Old Man. Tycho could never have known about the rings of Saturn, the polar caps of Mars, the belts of Jupiter or the millions of stars in the Milky Way.

It is usually said that the first telescope was made by a Dutch spectacle-maker, Hans Lippersheim, more or less by accident. This may or may not be true; but at any rate, during 1609 the news of the discovery came to the ears of Galileo Galilei, the great Italian whose achievements include pioneer work in experimental mechanics. (He did not, incidentally, drop any stones off the Leaning Tower of Pisa; this is a story of the Canute-and-the-Waves type.) Galileo was quick to see the possibilities. "Sparing neither trouble nor expense," as he wrote later, "I succeeded in constructing for myself an instrument so superior that objects seen through it appear magnified nearly a thousand times, and more than thirty times nearer than if viewed by the natural powers of sight alone."

Galileo was not the first man to use a telescope for astronomical purposes. In England, Thomas Harriott drew a map of the Moon with the aid of a telescope several months before Galileo began observing, and there were other pioneers too; but in perseverance and skill, Galileo stood alone. He was thoroughly systematic, and during the winter of 1609-10 he made a series of spectacular discoveries. Among these were the four bright satellites of Jupiter, the "multitudes of stars" in the Milky Way, and—most significant of all, perhaps—the phases of Venus.

We must pause briefly to discuss the phases of Venus, because it was in them that Galileo found his long-awaited proof that the Ptolemaic system is wrong. According to Ptolemy, Venus moves in an epicycle, whose deferent moves round the Earth; the line joining the Earth, the deferent and the Sun (EDS in the diagram) must always be straight.

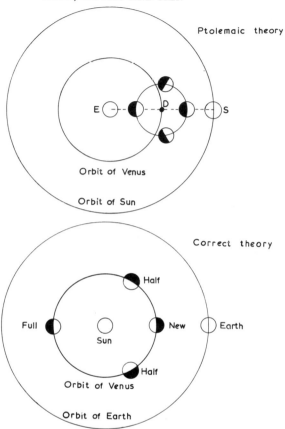

PTOLEMY *VERSUS* COPERNICUS. On the Ptolemaic theory, both Venus and the Sun were supposed to revolve round the Earth; the line joining S (the Sun), D (the deferent of Venus) and E (the Earth) was always straight, so that Venus could never show a full cycle of phases. On the Copernican theory, Venus could run through all its phases from new to full, so that Galileo's observations of the phases of Venus dealt a fatal blow to the Ptolemaic theory

Since the Sun can light up only half of Venus at one time, and this lighted half must always be turned sunward, the diagram shows that on the Ptolemaic system Venus could never be "full"; it would always be a crescent. Yet Galileo was able to see that the planet goes right through a cycle of phases, in the same way as the Moon.

Also, it had been regarded as axiomatic that the Earth must be the only "centre of movement" in the universe; everything was said to circle round this supreme world of ours. Galileo now announced that there must be at least one more centre, since the four satellites that he had seen through his telescope undeniably revolved around Jupiter. In fact, the Ptolemaic theory was failing every observational test that could be applied to it.

In the same year, Kepler published his first two Laws of Planetary Motion. The argument between the Ptolemaic and Copernican schools was by now fierce and bitter; Galileo had been a Copernican since his youth, but it was only after he built his telescope that he started to play a leading rôle in the controversy. Indeed, he seems to have regarded himself as something of a crusader, proclaiming the truth about the universe and giving proofs which, he felt, even the Church would have to accept.

He made various miscalculations. Less prudent than Copernicus, he made the grave mistake of thinking that the Church authorities would listen to reason; also, he was habitually outspoken, so that in many cases he gave offence when it would have been wiser to be tactful. On 21 December 1614, a Dominican friar named Tommaso Caccini preached a sermon in Florence in which he denounced Galileo and the other Copernicans, and expressed the wish that all mathematicians should be banished from Christian states as trouble-makers and fomenters of heresy. Another priest, Niccolo Lorini, wrote to the Holy Office in Rome condemning Galileo for trying "to defend an opinion which appears to be quite contrary to the sacred text", i.e. the Bible. If Galileo had been content to publish his discoveries and wait for the effects, he might have been left unmolested. Unfortunately for himself, he plunged whole-heartedly into the fray, and came into inevitable collision with Rome.

His worst error was to depend upon the goodwill of an old friend and admirer, Cardinal Barberini, who became Pope as Urban VIII. Barberini was a diplomat above all else, and he was not a man to be trusted. When Galileo published his great work *Dialogue on the Two Great World Systems*, in 1632, the Pope ordered that he should be called to Rome and put on trial for heresy. The ageing scientist was not ill-treated, and the threats of torture were probably not meant to be taken seriously, but at least Galileo was made to "curse, abjure and detest" the false theory that the Earth moves round the Sun. He was then removed to his villa at Arcetri and cut off from the world; during his last years he became totally blind. It was a miserable story, and was suitably capped by Pope Urban himself. After Galileo's death it was suggested that a monument should be erected over his tomb. The Pope forbade anything of the kind, on the grounds that the dead man "had given rise to the greatest scandal throughout Christendom".

After a time-lapse of more than three centuries it is difficult to decide whether the authorities at Rome were sincere or not. They certainly thought that Galileo was finding out much too much about the universe, and that his inquiries must be stopped. Needless to say, all that the Pope and his advisers did was to bring discredit upon themselves and their Church (though orthodox Catholics were not the only guilty parties in the story; in earlier times Martin Luther, the religious reformer, had been equally vehement in denouncing Copernicus as not only heretical, but also a fool).

Yet Galileo was the last famous astronomer to be persecuted in such a way, and within a hundred years the revolution was complete. The old order could not persist, despite the Church, because of the new spirit of intellectual inquiry combined with the new techniques being developed. Galileo's most powerful telescope was feeble by present standards, and cannot have been as good as a pair of modern binoculars, but it was soon surpassed, and more and more of the universe became available for inspection. It was natural, then, for fossil beliefs such as astrology to fade away; the prevailing mysticism was being replaced by something much more definite. And as time went by, men learned how to tackle the problems of the universe in a rational way.

Interlude

THIS BOOK IS not a full history of astronomy, and I propose, therefore, to pass quickly over the period separating the early seventeenth century from the present time. Yet the story will be hopelessly incomplete unless a few of the gaps are filled in, and it may be useful to give a general outline of the way in which men's outlook changed.

The discovery that the Earth is an unimportant planet came as a shock. Scientists were reasonably quick to adapt themselves to the new ideas, but the mental adjustment was a radical one, and it left its mark. Efforts were still made to show that even if the Earth had to be dismissed as a junior body, the Sun must at least be significant. Its distance was measured with fair accuracy in 1672 by G. D. Cassini, and found to be 86,000,000 miles; the real distance is 93,000,000 miles, so that Cassini was not very wide of the mark. The estimate was of the right order, and for our present purpose we are concerned with principles rather than details.

Telescopes were improved; national observatories were founded, and much of the old superstition was swept away. Linked with this was the realization

80

that the Earth is far older than had been thought, so that Archbishop Ussher's estimate of 4004 B.C. for the Creation started to look very naïve. Here, of course, the backward-pulling influence of the Church was very marked, and it was considered blasphemous to suggest that human life might have evolved from primitive mammals instead of being produced in the Garden of Eden. Men had to make yet another mental effort to accept that the universe is vast in time as well as in space.

A determined attack on the problem of star-distances was made by William Herschel, possibly the greatest astronomical observer who has ever lived. Herschel, a Hanoverian musician who came to England as a young man and made a hobby of astronomy, rocketed to fame in 1781, when he discovered a new planet—the world we now call Uranus. Its existence had been quite unsuspected, because there were seven members of the Solar System (the Sun, Moon and five naked-eye planets), and seven was the mystical number; what could be more satisfactory? But Uranus was a true planet, moving well beyond the orbit of Saturn and taking as long as 84 years to go once round the Sun. It had been seen several times before Herschel's discovery, but it had always been mistaken for a faint star.

This particular observation caused a change in Herschel's fortunes. He was made Court Astronomer to King George III, and he was able to give up music as a means of livelihood, even though his scientific salary was by no means princely. So far as star distances were concerned, he adopted what we call the parallax method, which need not be described here, but which was perfectly sound in theory. Herschel's instruments were not sensitive enough for the task, but during the course of his investigations he made several valuable discoveries— notably that of binary systems, each made up of two stars moving round their common centre of gravity in a period of years. Mizar, the second star in the tail of the Great Bear, is such a binary. Any small telescope will show that it consists of two stars, one rather brighter than the other, while there is a more distant naked-eye companion known as Alcor.

Herschel also put forward the first plausible idea about the shape of our star-system or Galaxy. He believed it to be flattened, with the Sun and its planets lying near the centre. This would mean that in looking along the main plane we would see many stars in much the same direction, so giving rise to the Milky Way effect which is so glorious a feature of the night sky. Herschel was wrong in placing the Sun near the galactic centre; really we are one-third of the way from the centre to the edge, but at least the general picture is not misleading, and it stressed once again that the Sun is nothing more than an ordinary star.

Herschel died in 1822. Sixteen years later the German astronomer F. W. Bessel applied the parallax method successfully, and was able to show that a faint star in the constellation of the Swan, known by its catalogue number of 61 Cygni, is roughly 60 million million miles away. Bessel's estimate was remarkably accurate; even so, 61 Cygni is one of our nearest stellar neighbours. The closest of all, Proxima in the southern hemisphere of the sky, lies at about 24 million million miles.

Figures of this sort are cumbersome, and we need a larger unit. This is provided by the velocity of light, which was already known to be 186,000 miles per second. In a year, light will cover almost 6 million million miles, and this unit, the light-year, is a convenient yardstick. 61 Cygni is about 11 light-years away, Proxima rather over 4 light-years.

Most of the other stars are much more remote. The Pole Star, which even non-astronomers can recognize, has a distance of about 680 light-years, while Rigel, the brilliant white star in the foot of Orion, seems to be 900 light-years away. Consequently, our views of the sky are bound to be out of date. It has taken light from the Pole Star 680 years to reach us, and we therefore see it not as it is now, but as it used to be 680 years ago, at the time when the then king of England was doing his best to conquer the Scots and the Welsh (a process which, it is claimed by some, is by no means complete even yet).

Indirect methods have to be used to measure distances of this sort, and Bessel had to confine his attention to our immediate surroundings, but his work proved that the Galaxy is even larger than had been thought. It was no longer possible to regard the Sun as important, and still another illusion had been shattered.

The nineteenth century was, overall, a period of steady progress. Photography came to the fore, and so did the astronomical instrument known as the spectroscope, which splits up light and is quite indispensable in modern research. The next major readjustment, however, was postponed until almost our own time, though the foundations had been laid much earlier.

In the sky there are some dim objects known as nebulæ, from the Latin word meaning "clouds".

Some of them are visible to the naked eye, and look like patches of gas; the best example is the nebula in the Sword of Orion. Others are subtly different, and give the impression of being made up of large numbers of stars, so crowded together that they merge into a continuous blur. From Europe, only one of these is visible without optical aid—the Great Nebula in Andromeda, which is admittedly a disappointing object when seen through a small telescope, but which is truly magnificent when photographed with a large instrument. Plenty of "starry nebulæ" were known before the end of the last century, and in some cases their shapes were spiral, so that they looked rather like Catherine-wheels.

The vital step was taken by E. E. Hubble, using what was then the largest telescope in the world, the reflector set up at Mount Wilson in California. Unlike Galileo's tiny instrument, it collected its light not by means of a lens, but by using a glass mirror 100 in. across; it was a masterpiece of mechanical skill as well as being optically efficient, and even today there are only three telescopes of greater aperture.

Hubble studied the individual stars in some of the spirals, including the Andromeda system, and was able to find out their real luminosities. This gave him a clue to their distances, and he found that they were so remote that they could not possibly belong to our own Galaxy. It followed that the starry nebulæ were galaxies in their own right, some of them just as large as ours. The Andromeda Spiral, one of the nearest galaxies known, is over two million light-years from us.

The implications are easy to see. First the Earth

had been shown to be unimportant; then the Sun became an ordinary star; now the Galaxy became a normal galaxy, one among millions. The change in outlook was complete.

Of course, it may be that there is a final step to be taken, and there have been suggestions that the whole observable universe, with its suns and galaxies, is simply one unit in a larger whole. But this is beyond our grasp at the moment, even if true, and we must await the results of further research. In any case, there could no longer be any objection on non-scientific grounds. During the years that have passed since Galileo first turned his telescope to the sky, we have at least learned the lesson of humility, and we have no pride left to lose.

Part II
THE PRESENT

[1]

In the Observatory

EVEN IN THE Space Age there are still many people who have completely false ideas about astronomers and observatories. It used to be thought that an astronomer must be unworldly and vague, presumably because he spent so much of his time gazing through telescopes that he tended to forget more mundane matters. This picture was never true, and today it bears no possible relation to the facts.

Admittedly, the astronomer cannot handle any of the objects in the sky (apart, of course, from meteorites which have ended their careers by hitting the Earth). Until it becomes possible to obtain samples from the Moon, which should be done in the foreseeable future, the only course is to rely upon sheer observation and deduction. But modern astronomy is not divorced from other sciences; it is linked with physics, chemistry and many others, including biology. The stars are the greatest "natural laboratories" known to us, and they allow us to study matter under conditions which cannot be artificially reproduced.

Quite apart from its association with navigation and timekeeping, then, astronomy is of practical

importance in our everyday lives, and this at once
brings the astronomer "down to earth", to use the
hackneyed term. Moreover, the professional astronomer spends remarkably little time in looking
through telescopes. Almost all his work is done
photographically, and for every hour spent in the
observatory dome there must be many hours of
patient, exacting desk-work.

Galileo's primitive telescope was a refractor; that
is to say, it collected its light by means of a lens
known as an object-glass, after which the image of
the object under study was magnified by an eye-
piece. When Sir Isaac Newton began his pioneer
investigations into the nature of light, more than
fifty years later, he paid great attention to the
worst fault of a refractor—its habit of producing
false colour, so that a white star would apparently
be surrounded by bright rings of varied hues, which
might look beautiful but which were certainly
unwelcome.

Newton passed "white" light through a triangular
glass prism, and found that he was able to split up
the beam, producing a rainbow of colours from red,
orange, yellow and green through to blue and violet.
He realized that the original light was made up of
all these colours blended together, and that the
triangular prism had separated them. Everything
depended upon the wavelengths of the various
component parts of light, because short wavelengths
were bent or "refracted" more than longer ones.

If we regard light as a wave-motion, the wavelength may be taken as the distance between one
crest and the next. Even for red light the wavelength
is too short to be conveniently measured in inches,
and the accepted unit is the Ångström, named in

honour of the last-century Swedish physicist of that name. Each Ångström is equal to one hundred-millionth of a centimetre, so that it is extremely small. Red light has a wavelength of roughly 7500 Å, while for violet the figure is only about 3900Å.

The shorter the wavelength, the more the refraction. Therefore, the blue part of the original light-beam is bent more than the red, and arrives at a different point on our screen, while the remaining colours of the rainbow will be appropriately spread out. This is highly instructive, but it means that there are difficulties with simple refracting telescopes. The object-glass tends to split up the light much as a prism will do, and so the blue part is brought to focus closer to the object-glass than the red part. The result is the appearance of false colour around any bright object, such as a star.

The trouble can never be completely cured, but it can be reduced by making compound object-glasses. The world's largest refractor today has an object-glass 40 in. across, which is very different from the tiny 1-in. telescope used by Galileo. Yet in many ways the refractor is completely outmatched by the reflector, which has no object-glass at all, but which collects its light by means of a mirror. Since a mirror reflects all the various colours equally, there are no irritating, gaudy rings, and moreover a large mirror is easier to make and support than a large lens.

The first reflector was made by Newton about 1671, though it is only fair to say that the principle had been described earlier by the Scottish mathematician James Gregory. Newton carried out his experiments because he could not see the cure for the refractor trouble, and in fact he never did solve

The 102-in. reflector at the Crimean Astrophysical Observatory, U.S.S.R.

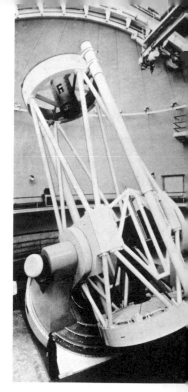

The mirror of the 102-in. reflector during final construction

it; but the reflector was a marked success, and was soon developed.

Nowadays, the world's greatest reflector is the Hale telescope at Palomar, in California, where the mirror is 200 in. across. The observer is carried in a cage placed inside the telescope tube, and so a certain amount of the incoming light is blocked, but this does not much matter, and in any case there is no way of avoiding it.

The 200-in. was ready for use in 1948. Previously, pride of place had gone to the 100-in. at Mount Wilson, also in California—the telescope used by Hubble to show that the spiral nebulæ were true galaxies, instead of being mere parts of our own star-system. Since then, various other large reflectors have been built. There is a 120-in. at the Lick Observatory in America, a 102-in. at the Crimea and a 98-in. at the new site of the Royal Greenwich Observatory in England. At the moment a 150-in. is being planned for the southern hemisphere, and will be sited in Australia, where it will be most welcome. By contrast, all the large refractors are rather old, and I rather doubt whether the 40-in. will ever be surpassed.

Let it be stressed at once that these huge instruments are designed not for studying the Moon and planets, but for collecting the light from very faint, remote stars and galaxies. Excluding the space-research teams, most modern astronomers are not particularly concerned with the Solar System; they want to learn more about the state and development of the universe as a whole, and for this purpose it is essential to reach out as far as possible. To use the 200-in. reflector for mapping the Moon would mean diverting it from the work which only it can do. The plate given here shows two photographs of the same part of the Moon, the crater Clavius, one taken with the 200-in. (on one of the very rare occasions when it was turned moonward) and the other obtained with a home-built 12-in. The gain with the larger telescope is not nearly so pronounced as might be thought, and to use the 200-in. for lunar mapping would be criminally wasteful. On the other hand, the amateur 12-in. could not hope even to see galaxies which can be studied in detail from Palomar.

Also, great telescopes are seldom used visually; their rôle is to take photographs. Unlike the human eye, the camera cannot normally be deceived. It can provide a permanent record which can be studied at leisure, and it is more effective than the eye, because during the exposure it goes on collecting light all the time, so building up more and more detail. Visually, no telescope yet made could show as much of, say, the Andromeda Galaxy as is revealed in a good photograph.

There is another point, equally vital. On its own, the telescope is limited, since it can never show a star as anything but a dot of light. Of course the stars look like disks when photographed, but these disks are not real, and do not relate to the sizes of the stars. Without auxiliary equipment, then, we should still know very little about stellar composition.

When Newton passed his beam of sunlight through a prism, and produced a rainbow stretching from red to violet, he had taken the first step in what is now known as spectroscopy, though he was quite unaware of the fact. Just as a telescope collects light, so a spectroscope analyzes it. The starlight is

The great crater Clavius, as photographed with the Palomar 200-in. reflector

The same crater photographed with Commander H. R. Hatfield's 12½-in. reflector in Sevenoaks

passed through a prism or some device which has an equivalent effect, and is spread out into a coloured band or spectrum. The spectrum of a star is far more informative than a simple image, and has led on to modern astrophysics, i.e. the study of the physics of the stars.

To produce a workable spectrum there must be sufficient light available, which is why a large telescope has to be used for examining the spectra of faint objects. With smaller telescopes the spread-out light becomes so feeble that the spectrum cannot be properly seen or photographed. So far, the Palomar 200-in. is in a class of its own; it can reach out to dim galaxies that no other telescope can find, and because long time-exposures are needed, sometimes extending over many hours, it has to be amazingly accurate from an engineering point of view. The slightest mechanical defect would cancel out all the advantages of perfect optics.

When the spectra have been photographed, the observing period is over, but the real work is only just beginning. The results have to be analysed, and this means that the astronomer has to be a skilled mathematician; in fact, astronomical mathematics are probably the most difficult of all. Nothing could be further away from the old, false picture of a man spending his nights "gazing at the stars".

It is probably true to say that the telescope and the spectroscope are the two essential needs of the astronomer; without them, his scope would be hopelessly limited. There are many other pieces of equipment, but I do not propose to describe them here, because I have not set out to write a comprehensive textbook. Suffice to say that a modern professional observatory has to include such items as laboratories, photographic departments, libraries, lecture and demonstration halls, and living quarters. Since it is absolutely necessary to avoid sky-glare due to artificial lights, most major observatories are set up in isolated places, frequently at high altitudes. (Incidentally, it was the brilliance of London that drove the Royal Observatory away from its original site at Greenwich to the calm of Sussex. The present site, at Herstmonceux, is by no means ideal, but it is about as good as can be managed without going outside the United Kingdom.)

Special branches of research need special equipment. For instance, large telescopes are not suited to solar research; with the Sun there is plenty of light to spare, and the main requirement is for a high-dispersion spectroscope—that is to say, an instrument which will spread out the light into a very long, detailed spectrum. Most solar observatories have "sun-towers", with the light-collecting mirrors and lenses on top and the observing station either at ground level or below. And despite the current emphasis on astrophysics there are still a few observatories where the Moon and planets come in for their due share of attention. At the Lowell Observatory, at Flagstaff in Arizona, Moon-mapping is one of the main programmes; for this a large refractor is ideal, and the Lowell 24-in. is in use every clear night when the Moon is available.

There is little in common between, say, Tycho Brahe's observatory of the late sixteenth century and the modern Palomar. Tycho had no telescopes, and had to depend upon measuring instruments and the human eye. At Palomar the equipment is immensely complex and immensely costly. Yet each was pre-eminent in its time, and each resulted in fundamental advances in our knowledge of the universe. Tycho's observatory fell into ruin centuries ago, but the story of Palomar may be only just beginning.

In our own period, two more branches of astronomy have come to the fore. Rocket research, which began fifty years ago even if nobody cared to take it seriously, has given spectacular results. There is also radio astronomy, where the equipment needed is completely different in design from that of optical astronomy.

The whole range of wavelengths is known as the electromagnetic spectrum. Of this, visible light accounts for only a small part; the other radiations do not affect our eyes, and so cannot be seen. On the long-wave side of the visible band, we come to the infra-red, and then to much longer radiations which are always known as radio waves. The wavelengths here are measured not in Ångströms, but in much more familiar units: centimetres and metres.

It so happens that most of the radiations coming from beyond the Earth are blocked out by our atmosphere, and the only wavelengths allowed through are those in what we call the optical window and the radio window. However, it must be made clear that there is no essential difference between visible light and radio radiation, except in wavelength; both are electromagnetic variations. And since objects send out the visible light by which we see them, why should they not also send out radiations in the radio part of the whole range?

In the 1930s some experiments carried out in America by an engineer named Karl Jansky showed that this is so. Jansky was not looking for anything of the sort, and he never followed up his great discovery; but after the war, radio astronomy developed rapidly into a major branch of science.

An optical telescope collects light and focuses it, so producing a visible image that can be magnified. Similarly, a radio telescope collects and focuses radio waves, but there is an important modification, because no visible image is produced. One cannot look through a radio telescope, and the information is recorded (usually) as a trace on a moving roll of paper. A radio trace may not look imposing, but it is immensely valuable.

The most famous of all radio telescopes is the 250-ft. "dish" at Jodrell Bank, but there are other patterns as well, some of which take the form of long lines of aerials. Each is suited to its own particular field of research, and during the past

A radio telescope at the Pulkovo Observatory, U.S.S.R.; this is one of many designs

In the control room of a radio astronomy observatory in Latvia, a radio trace from the Sun is being checked

twenty years some remarkable discoveries have been made.

The Sun is a radio source, which is not surprising. Many people watching television programmes or listening to sound radio have heard what is described as solar noise, and the uneven hissing or crackling is quite dramatic, but it should always be remembered that nobody can hear actual noise coming from the Sun. Sound-waves are carried by air, and there is virtually no air above a height of a few tens of miles, so that there can be no question of listening-in to sounds coming to us across the 93,000,000-mile gap separating us from the Sun. The noise is produced inside the receiver, and is one way (though not necessarily the best) of making the radio waves available for study.

At an early stage in radio astronomy it was realized that the stars, excluding the Sun, are not sources of detectable radio waves. Instead, there were some points in the sky which were found to be radio sources, but where no bright objects could be seen with optical telescopes. We have learned much since then, and it has been discovered that there are sources of various kinds. Some lie inside our Galaxy, and of these the most important is the patch of gas known as the Crab Nebula, which is nothing more nor less than a stellar wreck; it is all that remains of a supernova, or exploding star, witnessed by Chinese and Japanese astronomers as long ago as the year 1054. However, most of the radio sources are well outside our Galaxy, and I shall have more to say about them later. Much nearer home, it is worth noting that radio emission has been detected from the planet Jupiter, though as yet nobody is quite sure of its cause. All heated bodies radiate to some extent in the radio range, and this thermal radiation has been found with several of the planets, but Jupiter is active on its own account.

It would be quite wrong to suppose that radio astronomy will ever take the place of optical astronomy. Each can carry out researches that the other cannot, and we can gain our maximum information by combining the results of both. Obviously, a radio astronomy observatory is very different from an establishment such as Palomar or Greenwich, and it has been said, with truth, that the radio astronomer is above all an expert in electronics.

Then there is radar astronomy, which uses the same sort of equipment in a rather different way. The basic idea here is to send out a pulse of energy and "bounce" it off a remote body. The usual analogy (rather worn by this time, I fear), is to draw a comparison with a tennis-ball which is thrown against a wall and caught on the rebound. The comparison is not a good one, but I have never been able to think of anything better, and at least it shows the general principle.

Oddly enough, it is radar that has led to the best modern value of the Earth–Sun distance, or astronomical unit. What was done was to send out a radar pulse to the planet Venus, and then wait for the "echo" to be received. All electromagnetic vibrations travel at the same speed as light (186,000 miles per second); therefore, the time-interval between the transmission of the pulse and the reception of the echo showed how far the pulse had travelled on its way to Venus and back again. Once this had been found, the distance between Venus and the Earth was accurately known, and the other distances inside the Solar System, including that between the Earth and the Sun, could be calculated. The problem tackled so long ago by Aristarchus was taken up again by radar astronomers of the 1960s, with excellent results. The radar value of 92,868,000 miles for the astronomical unit is certainly very close to the truth.

Radar astronomy is limited in range, partly because of practical difficulties and partly because of the finite speed of radio waves. It would take a radar pulse over four years to travel to the nearest star, and another four years to return, so that a pulse transmitted in—say—1968 would produce no echo until 1976, even if such an experiment were technically possible (which, of course, it is not). But with pure radio astronomy, we are dealing in the main with bodies at tremendous distances, and radio waves can be detected from bodies so remote that not even the Palomar reflector will show them visually.

All these new developments have caused drastic alterations in our outlook. Telescopes, cameras, spectroscopes, radio astronomy equipment, rockets —all these have arrived to play their part, and, broadly speaking, only the telescope dates back for more than about a century and a half. Nobody can claim that the astronomy of today is a static science.

[2]

Planets, Satellites and Flying Saucers

THE SOLAR SYSTEM is made up of the Sun, nine principal planets, and various smaller bodies such as the moons or satellites which go round some of the planets. Broadly speaking, the system is divided into two parts. There is an inner group of planets, including the four relatively small, solid worlds of Mercury, Venus, the Earth and Mars; then comes a wide gap filled by many thousands of dwarf worlds known as asteroids or minor planets, followed by the four giants Jupiter, Saturn, Uranus and Neptune. Pluto, a curious body discovered only in 1930, lies on the extreme edge of the planetary system, and does not seem to fit into the general pattern, though as yet we cannot claim to know a great deal about it.

It is often said that a planet may be distinguished from a star because it does not twinkle. This is not entirely true, since when a planet is low down over the horizon it may twinkle quite strongly, but certainly its light generally appears more steady, because it shows up as a tiny disk instead of a mere point of light. However, anyone who has even a nodding acquaintance with the night sky will be able to pick out any planet which happens to be visible, because each has its own characteristics.

The two innermost planets, Mercury and Venus, are closer to the Sun than we are, and so have their own way of behaving. They are best seen either in the western sky after sunset, or in the eastern sky before dawn; they never remain above the horizon throughout a full night. Mercury is never very conspicuous (there is an old story, probably untrue, that Copernicus never managed to see it in his life!), but Venus is brighter than any object in the sky apart from the Sun and Moon, and at its best it may cast a shadow. This is because it is a sizeable world, only very slightly smaller than the Earth, and is extremely reflective; its surface is hidden by a dense, cloudy atmosphere, and of course clouds are highly efficient at reflecting sunlight. Moreover, Venus may approach us within 25 million miles, so that it can come closer than any other planet.

Telescopically, both Mercury and Venus show phases, or apparent changes of shape from new to full. Since they shine only by reflected sunlight, and since the Sun can light up only half the planet at any one moment, everything depends upon how much of the daylight side is facing us. As we have noted, it was this behaviour which gave Galileo his first definite observational proof that the Ptolemaic theory must be wrong. Unfortunately, the phase situation makes both the inner planets rather difficult to study. When at their closest to us, they are more or less between the Sun and ourselves, so that their dark sides are presented, and they cannot be seen at all except on the rare occasions when the alignment is perfect and the planet is visible in transit—that is to say, as a black spot against the Sun's disk.

Mercury has very little atmosphere, and is so close to the Sun on the astronomical scale that its daytime temperature is extremely high. It must be a barren, sterile world, and one can hardly picture that it can support life of any sort. Venus has proved to be a disappointment, because recent rocket results, to which I shall refer presently, indicate that the surface temperature is a torrid +500 degrees Fahrenheit or so. The attractive idea of a warm, moist Venus with luxuriant vegetation on its surface has had to be given up.

Beyond Venus in the Solar System comes the Earth, with its Moon. Properly speaking, the Earth–Moon pair should be regarded as a double planet instead of as a planet and a satellite, because the Moon is of considerable size; its diameter is over 2,000 miles, as against less than 8,000 miles for the Earth. Its average distance from us is 239,000 miles. A good way to picture the situation is to represent the Earth by a tennis-ball, wrap a length of string round it ten times, and then unravel the string, putting a table-tennis ball on the far end. This will give a reasonably correct model of the relative sizes and distances of the Earth and Moon.

Details of the Moon are visible with the naked eye, and modern maps of the surface are very accurate. There are grey plains, mis-called seas even though there is no scrap of water in them; there are mountains, valleys, and cracks or "clefts". Dominating the lunar scene are the walled circular formations always known as craters, which are probably of volcanic origin and are reasonably close relations of the terrestrial volcanic features known as calderas.

From the would-be space-traveller's point of view, the main trouble about the Moon is that it has practically no atmosphere. Its gravitational pull is much weaker than that of the Earth, because it is a less massive body, and so it was unable to hold on to any atmosphere it may once have had. Millions of years ago, the lunar atmosphere completed its leakage into space, leaving the Moon's surface unprotected. It is impossible to have any water on an airless world, and everything indicates that there is no life there. Future astronauts will have to exist under highly artificial conditions, and there is not the slightest prospect of turning the Moon into a sort of second Earth.

The same may be said of Mars, which lies at a much greater distance from the Sun: over 141,000,000 miles, as against our 93,000,000. It takes Mars 687 Earth-days to go once round the Sun, though its own "day" is only half an hour longer than that of Earth. The diameter of the Martian globe is 4,200 miles, which is intermediate in size between the Earth and the Moon.

Mars has always been the planet beloved of the story-tellers, who delight in populating it with creatures of all kinds, ranging from advanced versions of *homo sapiens* to the fictional beings known popularly as B.E.M.s (bug-eyed monsters). Half a century ago it was thought that conditions there might be tolerable, despite a low temperature and an inconveniently thin atmosphere. Unfortunately, rocket experiments made since 1965 have altered the picture very much for the worse, and we now fear that Mars is likely to be much more hostile than used to be thought. The surface is pitted with lunar-type craters, the atmosphere is very tenuous, and there is little free oxygen available. It is still quite on the cards that the dark surface areas

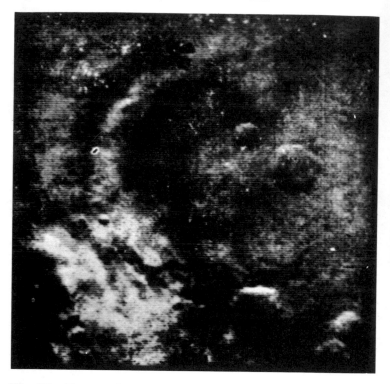

The Martian surface photographed by the American probe
Mariner 4 in 1965. The eleventh photograph, it is the best of
the series, distinctly showing large, lunar-type craters

visible in our telescopes are due to organic material,
and the white caps covering the planet's poles are
thought to be due to a thin layer of icy or frosty
deposit, but all things considered Mars is decidedly
unfriendly.

Far beyond Mars, and outside the belt of dwarf

worlds or asteroids, we come to Jupiter, giant of the Solar System. Here we have a body large enough to swallow up over 1,300 globes the size of the Earth, and it is no wonder that Jupiter shines brilliantly, despite its remoteness. Seen through a telescope, it shows up as a yellowish, flattened disk, crossed by streaky "cloud belts"; there are finer details, such as spots, which are constantly changing. The only semi-permanent or permanent feature of this kind is the Great Red Spot, which really is coloured, and which has been on view for several centuries. At the moment we have to confess that we do not know precisely what it is.

There is no mystery about the flattening. Jupiter is spinning very quickly on its axis, and its "day" is less than ten hours long; also, it is not solid in the conventional sense of the term, and is made up of gas, at least in its outer layers. Therefore, the rapid spin makes the equatorial region bulge outward.

Earth-type life cannot exist on Jupiter. Not only is there no solid surface, but the temperature always stays below −200° F., and the gas which makes up the outer layers is not inviting, since it is rich in hydrogen. The other three giants, Saturn, Uranus and Neptune, are modelled upon rather the same pattern, though there are differences in detail.

Saturn, the outermost of the planets known in ancient times, is second in size only to Jupiter. Its main distinction lies in its system of rings, which makes it undoubtedly the loveliest object in the sky when seen through an adequate telescope. The rings are made up of large numbers of small particles whirling round Saturn, and it has been suggested, without proof, that they are simply the débris of a larger body which wandered too close to Saturn in the distant past, and was pulled to pieces by the powerful gravitational pull. Though they are extensive, they are strangely thin, and it is thought that the ring-system cannot be more than ten miles thick.

Both Jupiter and Saturn have plenty of satellites. Jupiter's family consists of four large attendants, visible in any telescope, and eight small ones; Saturn's total is ten, of which the senior member, Titan, is larger than the planet Mercury, and is known to be surrounded by an atmosphere. The outer giants, Uranus and Neptune, are considerably smaller than Saturn, and have fewer satellites— five and two respectively. Uranus (discovered by Herschel in 1781) can be seen with the naked eye as a faint star, but Neptune (discovered in 1846) is below visibility with the naked eye. Pluto, the outermost planet, seems to be about the size of the Earth, and is so far from the Sun that it takes 248 years to complete one circuit.

This description of the planetary system is extremely sketchy, but it may serve as a lead-in to what is often thought to be the most fascinating problem of all: Can we hope to find other intelligent races within range of us? For the moment, I propose to deal only with life-forms of the sort we can understand, and we have to admit at once that the prospects are somewhat dim.

There seems little doubt that the planets were formed at much the same period, between 4,000 and 5,000 million years ago. The fact that they have developed differently may be due, in part at least, to their different original masses as well as to their different distances from the Sun. A non-massive body, such as the Moon or Mercury, will soon lose any atmosphere it may have produced, because its feeble pull will be insufficient to "hold down" the atmosphere. On the other hand, giants such as Jupiter and Saturn will be able to retain all their gases, including the lightest of all, hydrogen. The inevitable result will be the development of an atmosphere which is poisonous by our standards. The Earth has just about the right mass, and is at just about the right distance from the Sun, to produce an atmosphere of the kind we can breathe. Had this not been so, we should not be here.

However, there is no other planet where conditions are similar enough for Earth-type men to survive. This being so, what about those reports which have caused immense discussion in recent years—the stories about flying saucers?

The idea that the Moon and planets may be inhabited, and that the Earth may occasionally (or frequently) be visited, is not new. It goes back for many centuries, and it used to be thought probable that all our neighbour worlds supported advanced life. Even Sir William Herschel, discoverer of Uranus, was sure that there must be civilized races on the Moon, on Mars and even inside the Sun. Though by no means all his contemporaries agreed with him, he never wavered in his view and was still convinced of the existence of his Sun-men up to his death in 1822. In the following decade, a fantastic hoax perpetrated by a New York reporter, involving the "discovery" of extraordinary forms of lunar life, deceived a great number of people, including some scientists who ought to have known better. It was not until the mid-nineteenth century that the idea of Moon-creatures was finally discounted.

Visitations are another matter, and were not regarded so seriously. Novelists used the theme over and over again; for instance Bishop Godwin, in a book written in the 1630s, described how the Moon-men made a habit of sending any depraved children down to Earth, where there was already so much depravity that a little more would not matter. Coming to our own period, many Americans have rueful memories of the misleading broadcast of H. G. Wells' novel *The War of the Worlds*, transmitted just before the war, which led people to believe that the Earth had been invaded by monsters from Mars. But the flying saucer episode has been in a class of its own, and seems to belong more to mediæval than to modern times.

It began on 24 June 1947, when an American businessman making a routine flight in a private aircraft reported "a chain of saucer-like things at least five miles long . . . flat like a pie-pan and reflecting the Sun like a mirror". His story was widely publicized, with the result that other sightings were reported, and books on the subject started to appear. Of these, two in particular stand out. One was written jointly by two authors, Desmond Leslie and George Adamski; the other was produced a year later, in 1954, by Cedric Allingham.

In the first book, Adamski described how he had seen a Saucer land, and had made contact with the crew, who came from the planet Venus. Allingham's contribution was more or less along the same lines, but this time the "landing" was in Scotland instead of America, and the Saucer was said to have come from Mars. Unlike the Venusians, who subsequently showed themselves capable of speaking excellent broken English, Allingham's lone Martian was a poor linguist, and he did not stay for long. Judging from the only published photograph of him, we may assume that he kept his trousers in position by good, old-fashioned braces. Pictures of the vehicles were also produced, looking strangely like electric-light bulbs.

These books were among the first of many,[1] and there were, of course, the inevitable "investigators" who claimed that information available to The Authorities was being deliberately suppressed. And though the craze has long since passed its peak, flying saucer societies still exist.

I doubt if much time need be spent on the saucers themselves. Ice crystals account for most, and the rest are due to causes such as birds, bats, balloons, cloud formation and searchlight beams. The real interest is purely psychological, and no doubt the episode will continue to be discussed long after the last Saucer society has held its final meeting.

Let it be stressed at once that many of the flying saucer enthusiasts are completely sincere, a virtue also applicable to the flat-earthers, the circle-squarers and some of the astrologers. They see nothing irrational in claiming that a space-ship can come from another planet (either inside or outside the Solar System), fly around in our atmosphere, and depart without making contacts

---

[1] I will not digress to do more than mention those societies which are, so they claim, in constant telepathic touch with Mars, Venus or worlds across the Galaxy. However, one must spare some sympathy for the author of a book subtitled *Non-fiction. A story of a true experience*, whose wife subsequently began divorce proceedings on the grounds that the author's conduct with a lady from another planet had not been strictly in accordance with Earthly convention.

with any people except the favoured few. The photographs, of which there are many, are of two kinds; the electric-light bulb variety pioneered by Adamski and Allingham, and the series-of-disks type. In fact, flying saucer pictures have only one common factor; they are always blurred and out of focus!

It is natural for flying saucer writings to be linked with other "fringe" subjects. Even the mythical lost continent of Atlantis is brought in, and it has been claimed that the Atlanteans developed flying machines so like the modern Saucers that coincidence can be ruled out. Actually, the whole Atlantis story rests mainly upon the *Kritias*, written by Plato, who was at one time Aristotle's tutor. The *Kritias* tells of Ancient Atlantis as it used to be before the supreme disaster; the book is unfinished, and it can be put into the same category as the much later *Utopia* of More. Probably Plato's theme was drawn from the inundation of the small Greek island of Atalantë during an earthquake which happened during his boyhood. Atlantis has caused endless discussion, and the "position" is given differently by different writers; sometimes it is in the North Atlantic, sometimes in the South, sometimes as far afield as the Pacific Ocean. (So far as I know, nobody has yet suggested shifting it to Mars.) It is a fascinating story, but we must, I fear, class it with Olympus, Circe's island and the Golden Fleece.

The probable reason for the spread of flying saucer writings is that so many people would *like* to believe in visitors from beyond the Earth. This is a view which I share; nothing would please me more. And it is not entirely out of the question that other beings, immense distances away, have learned so much about space-travel that they are capable of crossing to the Earth, though I am bound to say that I am somewhat sceptical. At any rate, the evidence as yet is nil, and it is likely to remain so.

Unlike some forms of eccentricity, the flying saucer cult is quite harmless, and to attend a society meeting—as I have done on more than one occasion—is an interesting psychological experience. Moreover, the flying saucer enthusiasts are no more gullible than the flat-earthers, and less so than the astrologers. Above all, they mean well.

[3]

The Astronauts

IN THE SECOND century A.D., a Greek writer named Lucian produced a story which may well be classed as the earliest science-fiction novel. It was called the *True History*, because, as its author stressed, it consisted of nothing but outright lies. Its heroes were said to have been sailing through the Straits Gibraltar when their ship was caught up in a violent waterspout, and hurled as far as the Moon, where the adventurers were quick to become involved in a war which was being fought between the King of the Moon and the King of the Sun with regard to who should have first claim on Venus (the planet, that is to say; not the goddess).

Lucian did not mean to be taken seriously, and later Moon-travel stories were not classed as "science" even though some of them became very popular. They ranged from scientific treatises wrapped up in fictional form, such as the *Somnium* or Dream, written by no less a person than the great mathematician Kepler, to light-hearted frolics such as the *Man in the Moone*, by Bishop Godwin, whose hero was towed moonward on a raft pulled by wild geese. Then, just over a century ago, Jules

116

Verne wrote his classic *From the Earth to the Moon*, which was—and is—widely read by scientists and laymen alike. Verne proposed to use a space-gun for his Moon voyage, and this whole principle is wrong, but at least he kept strictly to the scientific facts as he knew them.

No astronomer of the 1860s seriously believed in the possibility of space-flight. Stories about voyages to the Moon or Mars were, it was said, idle dreams and nothing more. The same attitude prevailed in 1900, and a few papers written by a Russian school-teacher, Konstantin Tsiolkovskii, caused no real interest even among the few people who read them. Yet over thirty years later, Tsiolkovskii became something of a national hero.

Just after the First World War an American scientist, Robert Goddard, published a paper in which he suggested that it would one day be possible to send an unmanned rocket to the Moon. The ridicule poured upon him from all sides may not have been unexpected, but it was certainly one of the reasons why Goddard did not call a Press conference when he successfully fired the first modern-type rocket, in 1926. Goddard's original vehicle was small, and travelled at no more than 60 m.p.h., staying aloft for only a few seconds—and yet it was the forerunner of the space-ships of today. Subsequently, the Germans developed rockets as war weapons, and used them against England during the final stages of Hitler's war. When, in 1955, the United States Government announced that an earth satellite programme was being planned, the new science of "astronautics" became officially respectable.

It is amazing, in retrospect, to see how recent

this change of attitude really is. Though the astronomy of the nineteenth century was so much less involved than ours, it was fundamentally similar, but a hundred years ago there was no thought of practical space research. In passing, let us note part of a speech made by Dr. Dionysius Lardner to the British Association in 1838, in which it was said that "men might as well project a voyage to the Moon as attempt to employ steam navigation across the stormy North Atlantic ocean". The significant thing here is that Dr. Lardner was citing a lunar trip as something which is manifestly absurd, and in his day it was certainly out of the question, even though steam-ships were not long delayed.

A reluctance to accept new ideas is inherent in officialdom, and also in "experts" who are afraid of laying themselves open to criticism. This is probably why the then First Lord of the Admiralty wrote, in 1907, that the aeroplane would never become of any use to the Naval Service, and why the British Under-Secretary of State for Air wrote in 1934 that with regard to jet propulsion, "scientific investigation has given no indication that this method can be a serious competitor to the airscrew-engine combination", so that the Government would not be justified in spending any time or money on it. Astronomers as a class cannot be exempted from this attitude. After all, it was an eminent American astronomer, Simon Newcomb, who demonstrated in 1906 that no heavier-than-air machine could ever fly for more than a short distance, even though the Wright brothers had been doing so for some time past. Almost thirty years later another eminent American astronomer, Forest

Ray Moulton, said exactly the same sort of thing about the space-ship, and wrote that "there is not in sight any source of energy that would be a fair start toward that which would be necessary to get us beyond the gravitative control of the Earth".

In point of fact, the rocket can provide all the power that is needed to take a vehicle, manned or unmanned, from the Earth to the Moon. With un-piloted probes, it has already been done. It took a long time for the potentialities of the rocket to be realized; the first nation to do so was Germany in the 1930s. Of course, the German Government was concerned with war, not with the Moon, but the launching vehicles needed worked on the same principle, and work at the secret rocket ground went on apace. Yet even when the war was raging, we find the "expert" adviser to the British Govern-ment, Professor F. A. Lindemann (later Lord Cherwell), seriously claiming that all stories about Nazi rocket weapons were deliberate hoaxes. Not many weeks later the first V.2 weapons landed in South England.

The German attacks convinced even the Professor Lindemanns of this world that the rocket was something more than a scientific toy, but even so the space-research idea was not accepted at once. What finally tipped the scale was an official an-nouncement from the White House, in 1955, to the effect that small artificial earth satellites were scheduled to be launched in the near future. When the first such vehicle was actually sent up, by the Russians on 4 October 1957, the change in attitude was complete.

Therefore, our outlook today is widely different from that of fifteen years ago, and until the trage-

An American rocket launching in 1958 for a lunar probe

dies of early 1967, when three American astronauts
were killed in a fire in their capsule and a Russian
space-man crashed to his death while landing,
everything had gone so smoothly that the risks
were being forgotten except by those who were
actually concerned with the space projects. Judging
from various popular books and newspaper articles,
the conquest of the Moon ánd planets was only a
matter of time, and the term "exploring the universe" was widely used.

The *Gemini 7* capsule photographed from another vehicle in
orbit, *Gemini 6*, on 15 December 1965

The Earth seen from *Gemini 4* at a relatively low altitude

So far as exploring the universe is concerned, it is best for us to admit immediately that while we have to use our present-day types of rockets, our range is bound to be very limited. The Moon is within reach, and so are Mars and Venus, but these worlds must be regarded as local, and we cannot yet hope to probe much further, at least with manned vehicles.

Rocket power is essential, because it does not depend upon the presence of air. Ordinary flying machines cannot function except when there is air around them; for instance, the propeller aeroplane has to grip the air with its screw, while the jet engine depends upon drawing in oxygen from the atmosphere. The air-mantle does not stretch upward for very far, and so all conventional machines are useless for any kind of space research. But the rocket "kicks against itself", so to speak; as its propellant burns, hot gas is sent out of the exhaust, and so the rocket body is propelled in the opposite direction. Outside air is not needed, and is actually a hindrance, because it sets up resistance and has to be pushed out of the way.

There is another point, also. To break free from the Earth's gravity, a vehicle must work up to a speed of 7 miles per second, or about 25,000 m.p.h., unless it is prepared to go on using fuel all through the journey (which would be quite impracticable). Yet to move at 7 miles per second through the dense lower part of the atmosphere would be out of the question, because of the heat set up by friction against the air-particles. The rocket must start slowly, and work up to its peak velocity only when it is above the thickest part of the atmosphere. This is one of the many reasons why the old space-gun idea made famous by Jules Verne, in which the

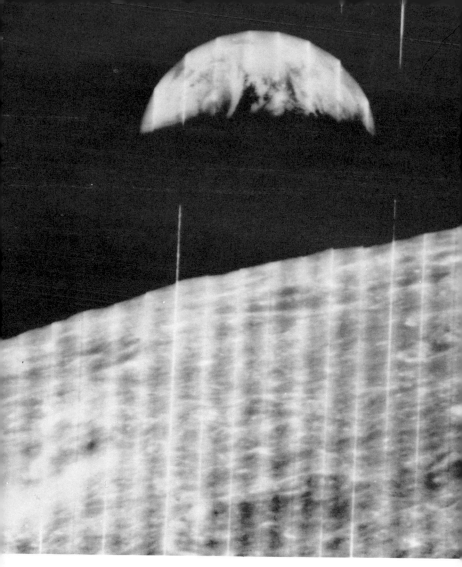

From *Orbiter* the Earth is shown as a crescent, the Moon appearing much the larger body. *Orbiter* was in the immediate vicinity of the Moon

The lunar crater Copernicus, photographed by *Orbiter* in 1967

projectile is simply fired off at escape velocity from the mouth of a huge cannon, will never work.

The Moon, at less than a quarter of a million miles from us, is so near on the astronomical scale that a journey there takes only a few tens of hours. Given adequate safeguards, there is no reason why a 1968-type rocket should not be good enough to take an exploring party to the Moon and back; the problems of air, food and water supply are easily soluble, as the entire expedition is bound to be a relatively brief affair. Not so with Mars or Venus, where the outward and homeward journeys will both last for months, and where the return has to be timed for a moment when the Earth and the target planet are suitably placed. In such cases, the "minor" problems will turn out to be anything but minor; and for still longer journeys, lasting for years (to the satellite systems of Jupiter or Saturn, for instance) I suspect that chemical rockets will not be usable at all. This is not to say that such journeys will never be made, because more sophisticated rocket motors will become available in due course, but there must surely be a long delay. Moreover, even these new-type rockets will be limited to the Solar System, and will be unable to take men to the stars.

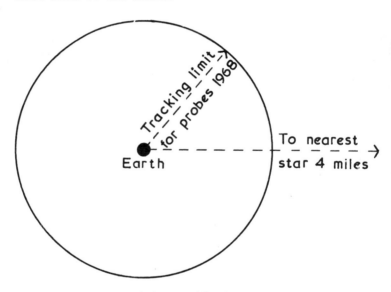

Probe Limit, 1968

EXPLORING THE UNIVERSE? By 1968, probes had been followed out to a considerable distance from the Earth; the limit is shown by the circle. Yet on this scale, the nearest star will be 4 miles away

In short: practical space research of the kind we can appreciate can take us no further than our immediate part of the universe. The diagram given here may help to drive the point home. The Earth is shown as a dot; the nearest star, excluding the Sun, is assumed to be 4 miles away; the circle shows the radius to which we have been able to follow out the unmanned probes with the longest range we have managed so far. So much for the grandiose claim about "exploring the universe". On the same scale, incidentally, the distance of the Andromeda Galaxy would be over 2,000,000 miles.

Yet the achievements of space research are already quite remarkable. We know far more about space conditions than we did before 1957, and, of course, we have close-range information about the Moon, Mars and Venus. One of the most important discoveries has been in connection with the Earth itself. Some of the early artificial satellites, beginning with America's midget-sized Explorer I of 1958, detected a belt of intense radiation around the Earth, and this Van Allen zone, named in honour of its discoverer, is of fundamental importance. It has also more or less killed the attractive scheme of a permanently-manned space-station circling the Earth at a height of a thousand miles or so.

There are many reasons for continuing with space research, and it is simply not a question of idle curiosity plus prestige, as some uninformed writers have suggested. Medical science will welcome a full-scale base on the Moon, where there is no atmosphere, and where all the radiations coming from space can be studied; remember that radiation plays a vital rôle in cancer research. Physics, chemistry, biology and other sciences will benefit

almost as much as astronomy. A major establishment of this sort cannot be unmanned, and this is
probably the main scientific reason why both the
Russians and the Americans are paying such attention to the man-in-space projects.

Astronomically, the rocket probes have already
been invaluable, and have been able to clear up
certain vexed questions; for instance, we now know
that the Moon has a surface which is pleasingly
firm, and is not made up of drifts of soft dust.
Admittedly, both Venus and Mars have proved disappointing, Venus because it is so hot and Mars
because its atmosphere is so unprepossessing, but it
is just as well for us to know the worst.

Much is being learned now about objects even
further afield. Once we send instruments above the
Earth's shielding atmosphere, the whole range of
wavelengths becomes available for study, and we
can find out a great deal about phenomena such as
the X-rays coming to us from distant parts of the
Galaxy. To quote the words of the tenth Astronomer
Royal, Sir Harold Spencer Jones, in a conversation
I had with him less than a week before his sudden
and deeply-regretted death a few years ago:
"Astronomy is going out into space."

The worst present-day problem is political, not
scientific. Were the various national space-research
teams able to work together, instead of separately,
the saving in time, money and effort would be
stupendous. I shall return to this point later. But
quite apart from politics, we cannot yet claim
definitely that a voyage to the Moon or any other
world can be made in the near future. Personally, I
think it can; I shall be surprised if the first Moon
landing has not been made by 1980, very disappointed

if it has not been managed by 1990—and I am prepared to believe that it may happen within five years
of the day on which I am writing these words (10
February 1968). But space is an environment which
is alien to Earthly life, and it is not impossible that
some hidden obstacle will hold matters up for a
long time. This, too, I am prepared to believe.

Most of the familiar "bogeys", such as meteorite
bombardment, have proved to be exaggerated, but
we cannot yet be quite sure about the cumulative
effects of radiations from which the Earth's surface
is screened. Certainly these radiations are not immediately lethal, and various astronauts have spent
many days in the thick of them without being
damaged, but we must not be over-confident about
delayed harmful effects.

Then there are the purely technical hazards,
which were brought home with such unwelcome
emphasis in 1967 with the deaths of the three American astronauts at Cape Kennedy, and the tragedy
of Colonel Komarov in his ill-fated space-ship
Soyuz I. It is quite in order to take a serious risk
with an automatic probe, since if it fails the only
loss is in time, money and labour. But men are not
expendable, and this alone means that the testing
periods must be protracted.

Until 1967, no lives had been lost in practical space
research. The remarkable stories about "lost
Russian astronauts" calling piteously for help are
psychologically interesting, but they have no
foundation in fact, and this is demonstrated yet
again by the fact that Moscow made no attempt to
conceal the Komarov disaster. It is worth noting
that at a comparable stage in development, aero-
nautics had claimed quite a number of victims, and

the fact that space disasters were avoided for ten years is a tribute to the efficiency of the planners as well as to good fortune. All the same, the events of 1967 have meant some serious re-thinking.

At the moment, it is enough to say that research is continuing as quickly as can reasonably be expected. Astronautics is no longer a dream, and it has come to stay, even though we must always be ready to admit that its overall scope is limited.

[4]

The Realm of the Stars

No TELESCOPE WILL show a star as anything but a speck of light. This is not because the stars are small; on the contrary, many of them are a great deal larger than our Sun. The difficulty lies in their great distances. All we can see are brilliant dots against the night sky; to show a star as a disk, we should need a telescope vastly bigger than anything we can produce at the moment.

For this reason, astronomers of a hundred and fifty years ago knew relatively little about stellar make-up. The Greek idea of stars being points fastened to a crystal sphere had long since been given up, and it was realized that each star is a sun, but this was about as much as could be said. It was only during the nineteenth century that new instruments were developed, leading on to the modern science of astrophysics.

An obvious first step was to study the Sun, which is the only star close enough to be examined in detail. The pioneer telescopic observations were made by Galileo, and he and others watched the curious dark patches known as sunspots, but unfortunately they could not tell exactly what caused

131

these spots—and we do not know even yet, though many theories have been put forward. Sunspots are cooler areas on the disk, with temperatures of "only" +4,000°C. (that is to say, 2,000° less than that of the average bright surface). They are associated with strong magnetic fields, and active spots are also linked with the short-lived, violent outbursts or flares, which eject particles and cause space-research planners some alarm. No doubt other stars show spots of the same kind, though we have no proof.

On its own, the telescope may be something of a disappointment so far as the stars are concerned, but the spectroscope puts a very different complexion on matters. As we have already noted, the spectroscope is a device for analyzing light and finding out what substances are present in the light-emitting body. Over a century ago it was already realized that the solar spectrum would yield plentiful information, and it was found that the Sun's most abundant gas must be hydrogen. This is not surprising, since hydrogen is the commonest substance in the universe, and exists in greater quantity than all the other elements put together.

The most important question was to find out how the Sun shines. At first there was little to go on; the surface temperature was known to be 6,000°C., but nobody had any real idea of the temperature deep inside the solar globe. Originally it had been tacitly assumed that the Sun is burning, but this idea is quite wrong. It is too hot to burn in the conventional sense, and moreover a Sun made up entirely of a substance such as coal, burning fiercely enough to emit as much energy as the real Sun actually does, would not last for very long; its life would be measured in a few million years at most, whereas we can show without the slightest doubt that the Sun is over 4,000 million years old. This is because we can put a lower limit to the age of the Earth, and to suggest that the Earth might be older than the Sun is not very logical.

After various blind alleys had been explored, the answer to the problem was found. Near the Sun's centre, in the "power-house" or core, the pressures and temperatures are tremendous, and strange things are happening to the hydrogen. Broadly speaking, the hydrogen is being changed into another substance, helium. Each time this happens, a little mass is lost, and a little energy is released; it is this energy that keeps the Sun shining. As time goes by, the amount of hydrogen becomes less and less, while the amount of helium becomes greater and greater.

I shall return to this point in Section III, when discussing the eventual fate of the Sun. For the moment, it is enough to add that though the Sun is losing mass at the rate of 4 million tons every second, it is in no danger of fading away, and it will not change much for at least 8,000 million years in the future. Fortunately for us, it is a refreshingly stable kind of star, not in the least prone to violent explosions or outbursts on a grand scale.

This cannot be said of all the stars, and occasionally we see what is termed a supernova explosion. Here, the energy-production inside the star becomes completely "out of control", so to speak, and the star blows most of its material away into space, so that it never returns to its original state, and the quantity of energy set free is quite staggering.

Supernovæ are not common; in recorded times only four have been observed in our own Galaxy, the last of which was seen (by Johann Kepler and others) as long ago as 1604. Astronomers would very much like to have the chance of studying one with modern equipment, but a supernova is something to be watched from a respectful distance.

Two of the four galactic supernovæ ought to be described further here, because each was significant. Taking them in the reverse order, we have the star of 1572, which was studied by Tycho Brahe and seems to have induced him to follow an astronomical career. At its best it was visible in broad daylight, though it lasted for only a few months before fading away. It caused a change of attitude, because Aristotle had taught that the starry heavens must be unchanging—and the sudden appearance of a brilliant star where no star had been seen before was visible proof that this idea was wrong. In fact, the 1572 supernova made another dent in Aristotle's reputation for infallibility.

Earlier, in 1054, Oriental astronomers had seen an equally bright temporary star in the constellation of Taurus, the Bull. It, too, was visible in full sunlight, and it, too, faded away after a while. As a star, it no longer exists—but we know a great deal about it, because we can see its remains. In the precise position of the 1054 star, telescopes will now show us a patch of gas, chaotic in structure, and still spreading outward from the old explosion-centre. We call it the Crab Nebula, and there is not the slightest doubt that it is simply the débris of the 1054 supernova.

We may talk of "the star of 1054", but in fact the outburst occurred long before that. The Crab

Nebula is 4,000 light-years away, and so the supernova exploded 4,000 years before the Chinese and Japanese astronomers watched it; in other words, we can date the event at around 3000 B.C. This again shows that beyond the Solar System our view of the universe must always take us back into the past.

I have already referred to the Crab Nebula, but I make no apology for returning to it, because it is so important to modern astronomy. It is a strong source of radio waves, and so far as we know there is nothing quite like it, though other radio sources also have been identified with supernova wrecks. For example, Tycho's star of 1572 is marked by a radio source, but there is nothing visible there on the same scale as with the Crab Nebula.

This is not to say that all the more normal stars are as quiet and steady as the Sun. This is not so. There are variable stars, which brighten and fade over short periods, either regularly or irregularly; there are stars that suffer outbursts which are extremely violent, but do not result in total destruction. These latter are called "novæ", as distinct from supernovæ. They are seen now and then, and may become quite bright. For instance, the nova of 1934, in the constellation Hercules, far outshone the Pole Star when at its peak, though by now it has become a faint telescopic object. Another interesting nova, easily visible to the naked eye, was discovered in July 1967 by G. E. D. Alcock, a British amateur who had been carrying out systematic searches. It lay in the constellation of Delphinus (the Dolphin) and was a fine example of a really "slow" nova.

We also meet with pairs and groups of stars. The best naked-eye example is Mizar, in the "tail" of

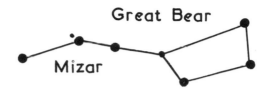

THE GREAT BEAR (Ursa Major), with Mizar. Close beside
Mizar is a much fainter star, Alcor, visible with the naked
eye; telescopically, Mizar is seen to be made up of two
stars—an excellent specimen of a binary system

the famous Great Bear, which has a much fainter
star, Alcor, close beside it. Any small telescope will
show that Mizar itself is made up of two, so close
together that without optical aid the pair gives the
appearance of a single point. The Mizar components
are moving round their common centre of gravity,
and are genuinely associated, so that they make up
what is known as a binary system. Incidentally,
Mizar was the first binary to be discovered; Riccioli,
the Jesuit who named the lunar craters and flung
Copernicus into the Ocean of Storms, split it as long
ago as 1651. By now, of course, the list of known
binaries runs into tens of thousands.

One of the most fascinating of all binaries is
Sirius, the brightest star in the sky. Sirius is not
particularly luminous by stellar standards, and is a
mere 26 times more powerful than the Sun, but it is
no more than 8½ light-years away, so that it is one
of our near neighbours. In miles, its distance works
out at around 50 million million. Very few known
stars are closer to us than Sirius, and most of these
are dim dwarfs.

Powerful telescopes show that Sirius has a faint companion, only 1/10,000 as bright as the brilliant star. Yet the companion is more important than it looks. It is a star of the sort known as a White Dwarf, relatively small (24,000 miles in diameter), but incredibly dense. A wineglassful of material from the Companion of Sirius would weigh several tons.

When the Sirius system was first investigated the results seemed to make no sense at all, but eventually the answer was found. In a White Dwarf, all the atoms are crushed and broken, so that the shattered pieces are packed together with almost no waste space, and produces material of this high density. Most normal stars may end their careers in the White Dwarf stage, and we may be sure that White Dwarfs are senile; they have used up most of their sources of energy, and are well on the road to extinction. They are certainly plentiful, and large numbers of them are now known, but their faintness means that we can detect only the closer specimens.

Just as we encounter small, super-dense stars, so we also find huge, rarefied stars which we call Red Giants. Here the diameters run into hundreds of millions of miles, but the density of the outer layers of such a star is very low. It used to be thought that Red Giants must be young, but we now regard them as comparatively old, so that they will collapse quite rapidly (by stellar standards) into White Dwarfs.

There is a tremendous range in luminosity among the stars, and we know of one supergiant, S Doradûs, which is at least a million times as bright as the Sun, though it is so far away that it cannot be seen with the naked eye. On the other hand, let us note that the Sun is not below average in luminosity, and it is far superior to the numerous Red Dwarfs. Also, there are many stars which are strikingly similar to the Sun in every way, and solar-type stars seem to be very common.

This is significant, because it is bound to affect our ideas about the distribution of life in the universe. Our own Galaxy contains a grand total of something like 100,000 million stars, and a reasonable percentage of these are not very unlike the Sun—and so why should the Sun be unique in being attended by a family of planets?

Much depends on how the Solar System came into being. As noted earlier, an old theory supposed that the planets were pulled out of the Sun by a passing star, and in this case Solar Systems would be rare, simply because the stars are so widely separated in space. If, however, we follow more modern theories of the Von Weizsäcker type, then it follows that planet-families are likely to be common. What can happen to the Sun can, and probably does, happen to other stars as well.

Not all planets will develop life, and an inhabited planet will have to move round the right sort of sun. Certainly a planet attending a variable star would be unsuitable, because there would be rapid and intolerable changes of temperature. Neither could we expect life upon a planet moving round one component of a binary system, unless the planet were so close to one star that the other star would not affect it.

Since the stars appear to us as dots of light, we cannot hope to see planets associated with them; but indirect methods have been used, and by now we can be quite sure that some stars, at least, have planetary companions. The best case of this is provided by Munich 15040, more generally known as Barnard's Star.

The individual or proper motions of the stars are very slight, but may be measured by means of photographs taken over relatively long intervals of time. Barnard's Star has the greatest proper motion known, and travels across the sky at a rate of $10\frac{1}{4}$ seconds of arc per year, so that it moves perceptibly from one year to the next; it takes almost two centuries to cover a distance equal to the apparent diameter of the full moon. Its distance is about 6 light-years, or 35 million million miles.

The remarkable thing about Barnard's Star is that its proper motion is not regular. It seems to be weaving its way along, though the irregularities are extremely slight and slow. There can be only one explanation; something is pulling on the star—and in 1963 P. van de Kamp and his colleagues in America showed that this "something" must be an invisible body with only $2\frac{1}{2}$ times the mass of Jupiter. This is too insubstantial for a star, and so we have every reason to suppose that the unseen companion is a planet.

The principle had been used earlier, and in fact the Companion of Sirius had been similarly predicted before it was seen visually. But so far as planets are concerned, the method is restricted to very massive planets moving round relatively lightweight stars. Certainly there would be no hope of finding a planet no more massive than the Earth, because the perturbing effects on the parent star would be too slight to be measurable. At the moment, we have to admit that Earth-type planets are out of our range.

We cannot make any accurate estimate of how

many planets exist in the Galaxy, but the total number must be very great, and many of these worlds must resemble the Earth in size, mass, temperature, and composition of atmosphere, so that they may be expected to support advanced life. Whether we shall ever be able to contact other civilizations remains to be seen, but the official view nowadays is that life must be widespread.

Modern investigations have confirmed that the Galaxy is a flattened system, with the Sun lying well away from the centre; our distance from the galactic nucleus is probably between 25,000 and 30,000 light-years. A bird's-eye view would show that the Galaxy is spiral in structure, and we have found that it is rotating. The Sun takes about 225,000,000 years to complete one journey round the centre, a period which has been nicknamed the cosmic year. One cosmic year ago the Earth was still in the Coal Forest period, and the most advanced life-forms were amphibians; even the giant dinosaurs lay in the future. One cosmic year hence the world will still exist, but it is impossible to tell whether mankind will survive, even if it does not commit suicide by indulging in nuclear war.

[5]

Island Universes

IN THE LATTER half of the eighteenth century there
lived a French astronomer named Charles Messier.
Like many other people, famous and infamous, he
had a hobby—in his case, comet-collecting. Night
after night he spent at his telescope, searching the
skies in the hope of finding a new comet and adding
it to his list. Altogether he discovered thirteen,
which is sufficient tribute to his patience and skill.
Louis XVI of France nicknamed him "the ferret of
comets".

Messier knew that some of the faint, misty objects
that he charted were not comets at all, but nebulæ
and star-clusters. Objects beyond the Solar System
did not interest him, and so far as he was concerned
the nebulæ and clusters were nothing more than an
unmitigated nuisance. He therefore catalogued
more than one hundred of them, so that he could
refer to his list while observing and decide whether
any dubious object could be a comet or not. Ironically, it is by his nebular catalogue that Charles
Messier is best remembered today.

In his list there were objects of all kinds. There
were true clusters, such as the Pleiades or Seven

Sisters, which are loosely-associated groups of stars. There were globular clusters, of which the only naked-eye example visible from Europe is Messier 13 in Hercules; systems of this kind are spherical, and near the centre the stars are relatively crowded, though of course they are still millions of miles apart. Also there were the badly-named planetary nebulæ, which we have found to be dim stars surrounded by vast gaseous shells. There were the gas-clouds such as the Sword of Orion. And there were the starry nebulæ, typified by the Great Nebula in Andromeda—Messier's Number 31.

Messier's contemporary, the great William Herschel, wondered whether these starry nebulæ might be separate systems, well beyond our own Galaxy. The idea was fascinating, but at that time there could be no proof. It was not until more than a century after Herschel's death that Edwin Hubble, using the 100-in. Mount Wilson reflector, showed that the starry masses are indeed external to our Galaxy. As we have noted, the distance of the Andromeda system is over two million light-years.

Since a nebula is a gas-cloud, the term "spiral nebula" is clearly inappropriate for the outer systems, and it has now been dropped. "Spiral galaxies" is better, but is rather too sweeping, because not all the galaxies are spiral; some are elliptical, some spherical, and some quite irregular in shape. Also, they are found in various sizes. The Andromeda Galaxy is larger than our own system, but there are also some dwarf systems which are on a very much smaller scale.

We must concede that even the closest of the galaxies visible from Europe are disappointing when

The Andromeda Galaxy, with the companion NGC 205, shown as an elliptical object at the lower right

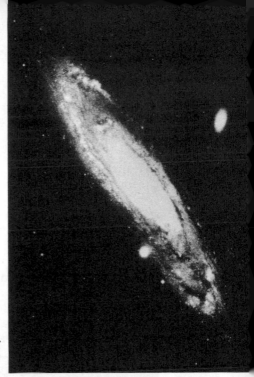

A more detailed view of NGC 205, seen with the Palomar 200-in. reflector

viewed through a small telescope, and the only spectacular objects are the two Clouds of Magellan, which lie in the far south of the sky and never rise above the European or North American horizon. To see the spiral forms of ordinary galaxies, it is necessary to study photographs taken with large telescopes. (The Clouds of Magellan, which look rather like broken-off parts of the Milky Way, are irregular.) With more remote galaxies, the individual shapes are lost, and all that can be made out are dim smudges of light, so that when looking at a picture of a galaxy-rich area it is not easy to tell which objects are galaxies and which are nearby stars, lying in our own system and appearing in much the same direction. The galaxies simply look slightly less sharp.

Very little is known about the life-story of what may be termed a typical galaxy, and we have no idea how or why spiral arms develop in so many systems, including our own. It is naturally tempting to think that there may be some sort of evolutionary sequence, so that an elliptical galaxy may develop into a spiral or vice versa, but there are serious problems to be faced, one of which is that the giant ellipticals are often some thirty times more massive than the typical spirals. Nowadays it is more generally believed that the different shapes do not indicate various stages of evolution, though the last word has by no means been said.

Observation shows that the outer galaxies contain objects of all kinds, including giant and dwarf stars, clusters, gaseous nebulæ, and unusual stars such as novæ and supernovæ. In fact, most of our knowledge about supernovæ comes from remote galaxies; as we have noted, the last supernova to appear in our Galaxy was Kepler's Star of 1604, before the telescope had been invented.

Let us return briefly to the Andromeda Galaxy, which belongs to our local group. The spiral effect is partly spoiled because we see it from a rather awkward angle, but the structure is clear enough when studied photographically. All the individual stars shown in the pictures are giants, because dwarf stars no brighter than the Sun would be too feeble to show up.

If we work out a scale model with the Earth and Sun separated by half an inch, the Andromeda Galaxy will have to be placed about a million miles away. Most other galaxies are much more remote, which is why they appear so unspectacular.

The Local Group is made up of the Andromeda Galaxy, the somewhat smaller spiral in the constellation of the Triangle, the Clouds of Magellan and more than twenty smaller systems. Other groups are known, and are called clusters of galaxies, though the term is not a very happy one and there is no connection with a star-cluster of the Pleiades variety. The total number of known galaxies is huge; the Palomar reflector is capable of photographing about a thousand million.

By vision alone, we could never find out much about the galaxies, but the spectroscope has proved an invaluable ally. The spectrum of a galaxy is made up of the combined spectra of thousands of millions of stars, and is bound to be something of a jumble, but it can be interpreted, and much can be gathered from it. In particular, it seems that apart from the members of our Local Group, all the galaxies are moving away from us, and the whole observable universe is in a state of expansion.

This brings us on to the Doppler effect, and there
seems no choice but to repeat an age-old, hackneyed
analogy. If you are standing on a pavement, and a
car approaches you with the driver clamping his
hand firmly on the horn, the note of the hooter will
drop as soon as the car has passed its closest point
to you and has begun to recede. Sound is a wave-
motion, and when the source of sound is moving
away, fewer sound-waves per second will enter your
ear than would be the case under more stable conditions. Therefore, the note of the car's horn drops,
because the apparent wavelength of the sound has
been lengthened. With light, where the speeds are
so much greater and the wavelengths so much
shorter, the effect shows up in a slight reddening—
that is to say, a receding object will look a little
redder than it should do. This is the Doppler effect,
named after the Austrian physicist who pointed out
the principle in 1842.

The colour change is very slight indeed, but the
effect shows up in the spectrum of a receding object;
the more obvious the Doppler effect, the greater the
velocity of recession. A body which is moving away
displays what is called a red shift in its spectrum,
and this is the case with all galaxies outside the
Local Group. The velocities are remarkably high,
and a galaxy several thousands of light-years away
may be receding at tens of thousands of miles per
second. It is a rule that more remote galaxies race
off more quickly than those which are closer to us,
and there is a definite law linking recession with
distance.

Let it be stressed that there is no hurry for us to
study the galaxies before they vanish into the
distance. Great though the velocities may be, they

The spiral galaxy M.64, in Coma, seen with the Mount Wilson 60-in. reflector

Quasar 3C-48, indicated by arrows, photographed with the Palomar 200-in. reflector

are still not marked when we remember that we are dealing with a universe built on a colossal scale. If you stand in London and take one step toward the east, you will not consider yourself significantly further away from the coast of America, but relatively speaking, you will have receded much more obviously than a galaxy will recede from Earth over the course of a century.

The idea of an expanding universe is deeply rooted in modern astronomy, and a few years ago there was no serious thought of questioning it. Expansion is still supported by most authorities, but it is fair to say that some uneasy doubts have crept in of late, due mainly to developments in the science of radio astronomy.

At a relatively early stage it was found that certain galaxies are very energetic in the radio range, and for a while it was thought that we might be observing collisions between separate galaxies— events which would certainly generate immense energy even if the individual stars seldom or never suffered direct hits. More recently, this intriguing idea has had to be given up, because no collision could provide as much energy as is needed; but nothing tangible has taken its place, and all we can really say is that some galaxies show evidence of having undergone vast explosions near their centres.

Mysterious though they may be, the radio galaxies are commonplace compared with the quasars, which have come to light only during the present decade, and which have caused theoretical astrophysicists an amazing amount of trouble. The story began when some radio sources were identified not with galaxies or supernova remnants in our own system, but with what seemed to be faint blue stars. When the spectra of these objects were studied optically, it was found that they were not stars at all; their spectra were quite different, and yielded red shifts corresponding to immense velocities of recession. If the Doppler effect is to be trusted, then an object of this sort may be racing away at more than 150,000 miles per second, indicating a distance of well over 6,000 million light-years. And to shine with the brightness we observe, then the object must be as luminous as 200 whole galaxies put together.

It was painfully clear that these objects were of new and suspected type. They were first called quasi-stellar objects or QSOs, but by now the term "quasar" has come into general use.

Our immediate problem is to work out how the quasars shine. Compared with galaxies, they are very small, which is why they are stellar in aspect. Yet how can a small body radiate as fiercely as a grand total of 100,000,000,000 × 200 Suns? It seems absurd at first sight. If we are not making a grave error in interpretation, a quasar must be drawing upon some energy-source about which we know nothing at all.

There have been many theories, each of which appears less convincing than the last. We can rule out phenomena such as chains of supernovæ; the ordinary nuclear processes, quite sufficient for the Sun, are pitifully inadequate; the idea that gravitational collapse may be involved in some way rests upon nothing more than vague thinking. Rather more promising, perhaps, is the theory that there may exist what is called "anti-matter", which is meeting normal matter head-on and causing the annihilation of both in a blaze of energy. But though the collision of an ordinary galaxy with an anti-matter galaxy would be drastic by any standards, and might release enough energy to produce a quasar, there are appalling difficulties, and it can hardly be said that the idea has any firm foundation. In short, the quasars are wholly enigmatical, and so far we have to admit that we are baffled.

Things might be better if we could assume that the quasars are not so remote as their Doppler effects indicate. If they are relatively local, they are presumably explicable; but in disposing of one problem, we have raised another. If the red shifts in the spectra of quasars are not Doppler effects, and do not indicate great recessional speed and great distance, then can we be sure about the red shifts in the spectra of ordinary galaxies? Perhaps not; and if this were the case, we might even have to give up the whole cherished picture of the expanding universe.

Few astronomers are willing to accept this, and the evidence—such as it is—still favours the expanding-universe theory, but it is not conclusive, and it depends entirely upon the Doppler effect. If this proves to be misleading, then we are back almost to where we used to be in the 1920s so far as our understanding of the galaxies is concerned.

Quasars may well hold the key to the whole problem, but there has not yet been enough time to study them fully, because they were identified only in 1963. Intensive research is in progress, and it is too early to speculate as to where this research will lead.

The photograph on page 147 shows a quasar, picked out by arrows because it looks so innocent. It is rather sobering to reflect that if modern ideas are right, we are seeing that particular object as it used to be before our world came into existence. What it is, and how it shines, we simply do not know—yet.

[6]

Toward Infinity?

WHEN WE SET out to examine the universe, we face the immediate difficulty of having to depend upon out-of-date information. Recently, I was asked whether I could prove that the Andromeda Galaxy exists. The answer I had to give was "No", because the light from the Andromeda Galaxy takes more than two million years to reach us. Visual observation proves that the Galaxy existed two million years ago, but we have no means of telling what has happened since then—and if the Andromeda system exploded tomorrow, we should not know about it until two million years hence.

Of course, I am not for one moment suggesting that the Andromeda Galaxy has "softly and silently vanished away", like the hunter of the Snark. There is every reason to suppose that it still exists, and will continue to do so for an immense period in the future; but direct optical evidence is limited, and it is worth pausing to mention the supernova which was seen inside the Spiral in 1885. We call it "Nova Andromedæ 1885", but in reality the outburst took place before men appeared on Earth.

It is mildly amusing, though perhaps not very

151

profitable, to list the views of Earth that we might have if we were equipped with a space-ship which could move at infinite velocity, plus a telescope of unlimited power. For instance, Vega, the brilliant bluish star in the Lyre, is 26 light-years away; if we could go to it (or, more plausibly, to a planet moving round it) in 1968, and take a close look at Earth, we would see the world as it used to be in 1942, with the German armies still in control of most of Europe. A view from the system of the star Gamma Orionis, in the Hunter's shoulder, would take us back to the days when Christopher Columbus was groping his way across the Atlantic, trying to find India but stumbling upon the New World instead. From Kappa Orionis, in the Hunter's foot, we might be able to see Brutus and Cassius preparing to murder Julius Cæsar, while if we want to watch Akhenaten's courtiers we could perhaps do so from a vantage point near the star Omicron^2 Canis Majoris in the Great Dog. From remote systems beyond our Galaxy, we could inspect the Ice Age world, the Earth dominated by huge reptiles, or the lifeless globe still without a solid crust. And to go out to the distant quasars would mean that we would be unable to see the Earth at all, no matter what telescope we might call upon. The Earth cannot be more than 5,000 million years old; therefore, to view the Solar System from a distance greater than 5,000 million light-years would mean seeing the Sun's neighbourhood as it used to be before the Earth came into existence as a separate body.

This may be idle speculation, but it is not completely irrelevant here, because the idea can be worked in reverse. If we examine, say, a group of galaxies 5,000 million light-years away, we are seeing them as they were 5,000 million years ago, so that in effect we are looking back into the past. This can tell us a great deal. In particular, the principle has cleared up a heated argument which raged from the early 1950s through to the mid-1960s.

The argument concerned what is generally called "the origin of the universe", but which I prefer to term "the development of the universe", for reasons which will be outlined below. Even now we do not know the answer to the problem, but we have certainly made some progress even if we are still working along faulty lines.

If the various groups of galaxies are racing away from each other, and if the speeds of recession increase with distance, it looks at first glance as though there may have been an original explosion in which the material now making up the galaxies was flung outward in all directions. It is hardly surprising that the evolutionary theory of the universe, which was put forward over forty years ago, is commonly known as the Big Bang theory.

According to this idea, all the material in the universe came into existence at one moment, and in the same region of space. The moment of creation must have been over 12,000 million years ago, probably more; it was followed by a Titanic explosion and a spreading-out of the material, so that general expansion is still going on. Some versions of the theory suppose that the present outward trend is due purely to the after-effects of the initial big bang, while others introduce a force called cosmical repulsion, which is the exact opposite of gravitation—and so becomes stronger when the distances between the bodies concerned are increased. Therefore, with more closely-packed bodies, such as the stars in our Galaxy or the galaxies in our Local Group, gravitation is stronger than cosmical repulsion and there is no tendency to expand, but when the separating distances reach tens of millions of light-years, as with the different clusters of galaxies, then cosmical repulsion gains the upper hand.

The idea of cosmical repulsion has been criticized on the score that nobody can explain it, but let us admit that gravitation is an equally mysterious force. And if we accept the Doppler evidence, and concede that the groups of galaxies really are racing away from each other, we must account for the expansion somehow or other.

After the war, a group of astronomers at Cambridge University proposed a completely different theory, according to which the universe has always existed, and will exist for ever. As old galaxies move beyond our range of vision, fresh stars and fresh galaxies are created out of material which appears out of nothingness in the form of hydrogen atoms. Therefore, the universe will always look much the same as it does now; a visitor returning to this part of space in—say—a million million years would see about the same number of galaxies as we do, even though they would not be the same galaxies. On the Cambridge picture, the universe is in a steady state.

The arguments between the evolutionary and the steady-state supporters raged fiercely, generating an amazing amount of spontaneous heat in the process! The only way to settle the matter was to examine the universe as it used to be in the remote past, and this could be done, because, as we have noted, a galaxy thousands of millions of light-years away will be seen as it used to be thousands of millions of years ago. Intensive research has shown that the distribution of the galaxies at such immense distances is not the same as is the case nearer home. Therefore, the universe is not in a steady state, and the whole steady-state theory has had to be given up.

To be strictly accurate, the observations were made by radio telescopes instead of optical instruments, because radio emissions are detectable over greater distances than for visible light. We can pick up the radio waves from objects too faint to be seen from Palomar, and it is radio astronomy which allows us to penetrate furthest into space. However, radio waves and light waves move at the same velocity, and so the principles involved are exactly the same.

To jettison the steady-state idea does not necessarily mean accepting the big bang, and a new rival has come to the fore in the guise of the oscillating universe, in which there is a long period of expansion followed by an equally long period of contraction. If this is valid, then the universe may have gone through the in-and-out process many times. But for the moment, let us return to the point made earlier. I suggest that we are not talking about the "origin" of the universe, as so many people claim; the term is quite wrong.

The one inescapable fact is that the material making up the galaxies, the stars, the Earth, your body and the kitchen sink exists; it must have come from somewhere or other. Either it has always existed in the form of atoms and molecules, or else it has been created—out of nothingness, presumably, since there would have been no previous atoms to convert. The evolutionary theory involves a sudden, universal moment of creation, while the oscillating idea could involve either a moment of creation or else a universe in which atoms and molecules have always existed. In either case, we are confronted with problems hopelessly beyond our mental grasp. We cannot explain how there can have been "nothingness" at one period, followed abruptly by a stage in which the universe contained vast amounts of material; neither can we understand a period of time which had no beginning.

All we can really do is to picture the universe as it may have been in the remote past, with its material already in existence, and then try to trace what has happened since. It is a study of development, not of origin. So far as the true origin of the universe is concerned, our ignorance could not be more complete.

Suppose that we put ourselves in the position of a totally alien being from another world, who lands on Earth and spends a brief period in some populated area such as London, New York or Tokyo. Our alien is interested in the origin of *homo sapiens,* and wants to find out as much as possible without actually getting into communication. He sees old men, young men, youths and boys, and babies in prams; in fact, he sees male humanity in all its stages of evolution. If he is intelligent, he will be able to deduce that a baby turns into a boy, a boy into a youth, a youth into a man, and so on. (He may make initial mistakes, and may suppose that a grey-bearded veteran is younger than a schoolboy—just as the astronomers did when they thought that a Red Giant is younger than a star of the Sun's type; but eventually he will learn.) He will therefore be able to trace the story of a man from boyhood to old age. But—and this is the vital point—how can he tell where the original babies come from? Without witnessing childbirth, or reading about it, he cannot know. And his knowledge about the origin of a man will remain nil, even though he will know a great deal about a man's development.

This is our present position with regard to the origin of the universe, and it is not easy to decide what the next step may be, though it is quite possible that the quasars will provide some all-important clues. At the moment the only people who claim a real understanding are the Biblical Fundamentalists, who say simply that God created the world and that there is nothing more to be added.

Certainly, this attitude leaves little room for discussion. In the Bible, the book of Genesis sums up the whole process of the origin of the universe in a few paragraphs, and so far as the stars are concerned says merely that God "made the stars also". The fundamentalists, of whom there are still a surprising number, are quite ready to leave the problem there, and to regard any further inquiries as irreligious. This sort of attitude was easy to understand in mediæval times, but it is not easy to understand now. Without curiosity, the human mind would surely stagnate.

Moreover, there is the underlying theme—not stated, but tacitly assumed—that the Sun, Moon and stars were created for the special benefit of Man. All the world's great religions have their own pictures of the creation, and Christianity does not by any means have the monopoly, but in theological arguments it is fair to say that science plays little part. In general, religion has not been noted for its sympathetic attitude toward intellectual progress, and there are the examples, widely separated in time, of Anaxagoras in Athens, Galileo in Rome, and the schoolmasters who taught the theory of evolution in the State of Tennessee.

Of course, it would be too extreme to suggest that modern religion is still fighting whole-heartedly against the progress of science, and in most countries the religious eccentrics are in a great minority. But the attitude does persist in some quarters, and it is not helpful. The fundamentalists give an excellent proof of this; to say complacently that the universe has been created by divine will, and leave matters there, is the outlook of an ostrich. The wish to learn is by no means sinful according to any logical standards.

We are still taking a very parochial view. During the past few decades it has become clear that life must be widespread in the universe, and that we on Earth represent a lowly form. When we consider an overall "divine force", we must remember that it covers the whole of the universe, not merely our own tiny and insignificant world. Beings on other planets, moving round other stars, will have their own ideas about how the universe came into being. Primitive peoples will attribute the Creation to their own particular god or gods; more developed societies will start to make inquiries; perhaps really advanced civilizations will find some of the correct answers. On Earth, we have only just started to emerge from the primitive stage, and we cannot yet come to any worth-while conclusions.

Neither, for that matter, can we decide just how large the universe really is. If the speeding-away of the galaxies continues to become greater with increased distance from us, then we must reach a point at which a galaxy is moving away from us at the speed of light—so that it will remain invisible; its light can never reach us, and from our point of view it might as well not exist. The indications are that this critical distance is set between 10,000 and 15,000 million light-years, which therefore marks the boundary of the observable universe, though these figures are decidedly uncertain and there may be errors in our reasoning.

In any case, this limit can hardly mark the end of the universe; and can "space" have an end? Or can it be that the universe we can observe is nothing more than a part of a still greater whole? Here, again, we have to admit that we do not know.

Perhaps there is another lesson to be learned from all this. In Greek times, the philosophers were modestly confident that they knew a great deal about the universe, with its central Earth, its stars fixed to a crystal sphere, and so on. The more we have found out since those days, the more we realize that we have hardly touched on the crucial problems, but we still think that in some ways we are on the right track. This is our view in 1968. By 1998, shall we have been forced to concede that our knowledge is even more limited that we have been accustomed to believe? This is quite possible; scientific history has a habit of repeating itself, in principle if not in detail. Time will tell.

Interlude

THE ASTRONOMY OF 1800 was, by modern standards, primitive. Admittedly, much had been learned, and in particular the distance-scale of the universe had been worked out—not accurately, but at least to the right order. On the other hand, the "essentials" of today, such as photography and spectroscopy, had not arrived, and the leading astronomer of the time, Sir William Herschel, was firmly maintaining that the Sun contained a cool, pleasant zone in which intelligent beings must live.

Developments during the subsequent hundred and seventy years or so have been dramatic, and there is no reason why this rate of progress should not be continued. What, then, is likely to happen during the rest of the twentieth century, and in the centuries to come?

Theories will be put forward, but no theory is of the slightest use unless it is backed by facts, and the observer has a vital rôle to play. He must have the best equipment possible; nothing can replace the telescope as a fundamental instrument, but auxiliary equipment must also be developed, notably in the field of electronics. Moreover, astronomy has

already become space-minded, and interplanetary
flight must presumably come before long.

A writer of fifty years ago would have been classed
as a crank if he had seriously claimed that by 1968
it would be possible to study lunar photographs
taken from the surface of the Moon itself. In making
speculations with regard to the coming fifty years,
I fully realize that I am laying myself open to the
same sort of criticism as I encountered in 1939,
when I suggested that earth satellites would be
launched before 1960. I realize, too, that many of my
guesses will be very wide of the mark. But come
what may, there seems little doubt that progress
between now and A.D. 2000 will be even more spectacular than the progress that has taken place since
the end of the war. It is an exciting prospect.

Part III

THE FUTURE

[1]

"More Light!"

DURING THE FIRST World War, the 100-in. reflector came into operation at Mount Wilson in the United States, far away from the scene of battle. During the next couple of decades it proved its worth time and time again; it, and it alone, could have allowed Hubble to show that the "starry nebulæ" are in fact external galaxies. Then, after the Germans had been beaten for the second time and the nations were settling down to an uneasy peace, the 200-in. reflector was completed at Palomar. It also has been responsible for fundamental advances, and up to the present time it has remained in a class of its own. It can reach much further into space than any other telescope, and if we are to study really remote objects, such as quasars, the 200-in. is essential.

This being so, it would seem that the obvious course is to construct a 300-in. reflector, or even a 400-in., so extending our range. Unfortunately, this is not nearly so straightforward a matter as it may sound.

Both the Mount Wilson and Palomar reflectors were due largely to the energy and persistence of the American astronomer George Ellery Hale. It has been said that Hale's constant cry was for "More light!" and he knew, only too well, that in astronomy nothing can take the place of really large telescopes. Of course, a huge reflector costs an immense sum of money. Hale persuaded friendly millionaires to finance the projects (to say nothing of various smaller instruments), but millionaires are less common now than they used to be, and we must face the fact that any comparable venture at the present time must be financed by a Government.

This raises obvious difficulties. Most Governments are very willing to expend vast sums of money upon armaments and the like, but not nearly so ready to make dollars, pounds or roubles available for peaceful scientific research. Taking the events of the past few years as a guide, one must admit that the total money spent upon the Vietnam war, farcical sanctions against Rhodesia, and cancelled Government aircraft projects would have paid for hundreds of large telescopes—after releasing immense sums to "feed the starving millions", to use the popular cry. To meet criticism halfway, let me emphasize that I would be the last to advocate giving large telescopes any priority over the relief of human distress. But given the choice between a new 200-in. reflector and an extra bombing raid upon some much-battered town, I would unhesitatingly opt for the reflector. (Also, nations with "starving millions" seem to be able to afford to spend a great deal of money upon modern-type armaments!)

On the other hand, it is by no means certain that a 300-in. or 400-in. reflector is a practicable possibility. First, it would be extremely hard to make. The Palomar telescope, appropriately named in honour of George Ellery Hale, is a masterpiece of optics and engineering; it has been said that the mechanical problems were as hard to solve as those of optics, and certainly there is no point in having a large mirror unless it can be accurately positioned and guided. But we also have to reckon with the effects of the Earth's atmosphere, which, to astronomers, is a major nuisance.

The atmosphere extends upward for well over a thousand miles, but for most practical purposes we can neglect all but the lower layers. To lessen the "dirtiness" and unsteadiness of the air, most large observatories are built upon mountains; for instance, the Pic du Midi Observatory, in the French Pyrenees, is almost 10,000 ft. above sea level. Yet this is only a partial remedy; and the larger the telescope, the worse become the effects of turbulence. Even if placed at the best possible site, a 300-in. reflector would not perform to its maximum capacity except on a limited number of nights per year. Moreover, no telescope set up on the surface of the Earth can extend its range beyond the narrow optical window—that is to say, the small part of the electromagnetic spectrum to which our atmosphere is not opaque.

To make this quite clear, let us recapitulate briefly. Radiations of all wavelengths come to us from space, but most of them are blocked by the layers in the upper air, and so never penetrate to ground level. Visible light can pass through, and so can some kinds of radio waves, but the rest of the radiations cannot. No matter how large the telescope, this problem cannot be overcome, and the only solution is to take our equipment above the screening layers.

Up to the present time, there are too few large telescopes (that is to say, reflectors of apertures from about 100 in. upward) to cope with all the work that needs to be done. With the Palomar instrument, every night is allotted to some astronomer for specific research upon some problem regarded as of genuine importance; if his allotted nights turn out to be cloudy, the luckless astronomer must make a fresh application and wait for his turn with as much patience as he can muster. Certainly the telescope can never be spared for observations of the Moon and planets, our neighbours in the universe. Its unique light-gathering power must be utilized to the full, which means that it is always directed to stellar objects. It is seldom or never used visually; all its time is spent in taking photographs, either of stars or galaxies or of their spectra. To a lesser extent, the same is true of all other giant telescopes. The procedure is perfectly logical, and it would be unscientific to suggest any other course.

All the great reflectors now in use lie in the Earth's northern hemisphere. This means that they cannot examine objects in the far south of the sky, such as the fascinating Clouds of Magellan. This means that our information is not complete, and a large southern telescope is an urgent necessity. In 1967 it was announced that a 150-in. reflector will be constructed for Australia, and this is a major step in the right direction, but there can be no doubt that more telescopes of this size are needed yet. It would be far better to have half a dozen 100-in. reflectors than one 400-in., even if a 400-in. could be made and used successfully.

I have said little about refractors, which are less in favour nowadays except for special purposes.

Whether any more giant refractors will be built seems rather doubtful, because in convenience and in sheer light-grasp they cannot compare with reflectors. It would be very nice to have, say, a 100-in. refractor, but it could not be made, and a mounting for it would present insuperable difficulties, because a lens of such size would distort under its own weight. The largest object-glass ever made, a 49-in., proved to be a total failure. It was shown at the Paris Exhibition in 1901, but it was never used for serious research, and I believe that it is now stored in the cellars of the Paris Observatory, where it will doubtless remain.

The immediate future, then, should be the age of more 100-in. to 200-in. reflectors. Larger than this we may not be able to go, so long as we are content to keep the equipment at ground level. Radio telescopes can be made to larger sizes, but there are difficulties here too, and there is no evading the limits imposed by the blocking-out effect of the upper atmosphere. To overcome this restriction, we must return to the prospects opened up by space research.

The modest balloon has its uses. Instruments have been flown up to 80,000 ft. or so, above the densest part of the air, and have yielded valuable information. But to study the full range of wavelengths, we must go up higher still, and this means using rocket power, since nothing except the rocket will function beyond the atmosphere. Various telescopes of small size have already been flown with success, but the ultimate aim is to have a large telescope in operation above the atmosphere, preferably with a human observer in attendance.

A "disembodied" telescope, so to speak, would be

impracticable for many reasons, and one suggestion, very popular in the 1940s and early 1950s, was to construct a space-station, which would move round the Earth at a height of roughly 1,000 miles, and would be manned by a permanent crew. Wernher von Braun, the great German rocket pioneer, published elaborate designs for such a station. It was to be shaped like a wheel, with the crew quarters in the rim; rotation of the wheel would provide artificial gravity in the form of centrifugal force, and the whole station was to be built in space after the various parts had been sent up separately by rocket power.

The idea did not seem particularly fantastic to those who believed in space-research, and it was undeniably attractive. The station would serve as an observatory, physical and biological laboratory, weather bureau, radio relay, and refuelling base for space-ships bound for the Moon and planets. There would presumably be no difficulty in sending ferry-rockets between the station and the Earth, so that the crew members could be relieved at set intervals. Too long a spell in space might have adverse effects upon a man's health, but shorter periods would, it was said, do no harm. Serious astronautical planners wrote that given enough funds, the station could be in orbit before 1980, provided that no unforeseen difficulties arose.

In fact, one major difficulty has arisen. In 1958 the first successful American satellite, *Explorer I*, sent back information to the effect that the Earth is encircled by a zone of intensive radiation, now named after James van Allen, who was closely concerned with the research. A manned vehicle going through the Zone en route for the Moon would be unaffected, because the time spent in the thick of the radiation would be brief, but to stay in the "danger area" for very long would be most unwise. The van Allen Zone is in itself enough to affect all plans for a permanently-manned station anywhere in the region.

Also, it was thought in the early 1950s that to send a rocket direct from the Earth to the Moon and back again would need more fuel than could be carried, so that a manned lunar probe would have to refuel on the way. The journey would thus have been accomplished in several steps; Earth to station in a ferry rocket, station to Moon in a lunar ship, Moon back to station, and from station home to Earth in the ferry. Since then, rocketry has made great strides, and it looks as though vehicle-changing and refuelling techniques will not be necessary after all.

If a station could be put into an orbit outside the van Allen Zone, it would of course be usable for the other purposes suggested earlier; but in my view, at least, it is not likely to be built. It would have no marked advantages over a scientific base constructed on the surface of the Moon, and it would have numerous drawbacks.

True, the distance from Earth would be much less, and emergency returns would be quicker, but all things considered it is not much more difficult to bring a vehicle back from the Moon than to bring it back from an orbiting station. Eventually, the return from the Moon may be the easier, because rocket bases will be established there, and full-scale launching drill will be possible.

On the Moon, future astronomers will not be troubled by atmosphere. To describe the lunar world as "airless" is correct for all practical purposes, and moreover the surface gravity has only one-sixth of its Earth value, so that all parts of a telescope will be very light. This should reduce some of the engineering problems, though there will be some awkward factors too; the night temperature is appallingly low, and the materials used for telescope construction will have to be carefully chosen.

With no atmospheric shield, a telescope will have greatly increased efficiency, so that a 200-in. reflector operating from the Moon will be able to probe much further than the Hale reflector can do from its site on Palomar Mountain. In fact, our range would be extended so much that we might at last learn something about the most remote parts of the observable universe, which brings us back to the problems of how the universe has evolved. So far, we cannot study quasars or galaxies near the edge of what we assume to be the observable universe, and we cannot be sure that the rule of greater-distance, greater-velocity of recession holds good all the way, but a lunar telescope ought to tell us. Also, the limitations on aperture will not apply there; why not have a 400-in., a 500-in. or even a 1,000-in.?

Generally speaking, the same arguments apply to radio telescopes, where the low lunar surface gravity will be extremely useful, and where there can be no winds or storms to shake the huge but delicate pieces of equipment. There is no weather on the Moon, and the only obvious hazard is the great range in temperature between day and night, which will cause various materials to swell and shrink. Even this may be avoided to some extent by setting up the equipment in the polar regions of the Moon, where the night temperature is the same as for the equator, but where the daytime heat is never great.

There are excellent reasons for claiming that the space-station idea has fallen into official disfavour, to be replaced by the much grander concept of a fully-fledged observatory-cum-laboratory upon the Moon. Yet it would be quite wrong to let one's imagination run riot, and assume that the first successful lunar trips will be followed quickly by the setting-up of a major scientific base. So far as we know, the Moon will not provide any materials which will be of real help to us—apart from firm ground, which is of course essential. To take all the parts for a telescope, send them to the Moon, and assemble them will be a tremendous task indeed, and it belongs to the latter part of the twentieth century. Neither can we neglect the unpleasant possibility that some hidden difficulty will cause a major delay in all our plans.

But despite the obstacles, there must be high hope that the lunar observatory, equipped with a really powerful telescope, will be in action within the next few decades. When it is operating, we shall be able to learn more about the remote parts of the universe than we have any chance of doing at present. Admittedly, the whole project still sounds somewhat fantastic—but certainly no more fanciful than a probe such as Luna 9 or Surveyor would have seemed to an orthodox, sober-minded astronomer of forty years ago. Before A.D. 2000, George Ellery Hale's call for "More light!" may have been well and truly answered.

The Search for Life

OF ALL THE puzzles facing mankind, perhaps the most fascinating is that of life beyond the Earth. I have touched on this problem earlier in the present book, but I do not apologize for returning to it and discussing it in rather more detail. To suppose that mankind is the only intelligence in the universe is clearly absurd, but where can we look for other races with whom we might be able to communicate?

The answer must be, unhappily: "A very long way away"—so far, indeed, that rocket contact is quite out of the question. If we reject flying saucers and the like, we are bound to concede that there can be no intelligent life in the Solar System except on Earth, and this means that our investigations must be carried through by observation and deduction alone. Rockets cannot help us; perhaps they never will.

Life of Earthly type requires a fairly even temperature, a moderately dense atmosphere containing free oxygen, and adequate water supply. In the Solar System, only the Earth satisfies all these conditions. Of the other possible candidates, Mercury, the Moon, and most of the satellites of the giant planets are without atmosphere; the giants themselves have no solid surfaces, and are intolerably cold; Pluto is ruled out on the score of low temperature and probable lack of atmosphere. Only Venus and Mars remain to be considered seriously.

Until 1962, Venus was regarded by some astronomers (including myself) as the more promising. Its atmosphere was known to be rich in carbon dioxide gas, and the surface temperature was presumably rather high, but there was no valid reason for doubting that oceans might exist there. On Earth, life first appeared in the warm seas in the days when our atmosphere, too, contained a high percentage of carbon dioxide. Why, then, should not Venus be a world upon which life was just starting to develop?

It was an attractive idea, but the information drawn from the *Mariner II* probe of late 1962 did not support it, and the Russian vehicle *Venus 4*, which made a successful soft landing there in 1967, confirmed that the surface temperature is extremely high—in which case there can be no liquid water, while life of terrestrial type must be regarded as highly improbable.

Mars has always presented different problems. Sixty years ago, Percival Lowell, the great American astronomer who founded Flagstaff Observatory in Arizona, was firmly maintaining that the streaky features known to everyone as the Martian canals were artificial waterways, built by intelligent beings to provide a planet-wide irrigation system. No serious astronomer supports this idea nowadays, and indeed it was regarded with considerable scepticism even in Lowell's lifetime, but the *Mariner IV*

results of 1965 have even cast doubt upon the vegetation theory of the Martian dark areas. The
planet's atmosphere has proved to be depressingly
thin, and to be made up largely of carbon dioxide.
The brilliant-brained, ultra-civilized Martians have
made their exit from scientific thought, regretted
by all.

If there are no intelligent beings on Mars or Venus
(or, of course, on the Moon), it seems rather pointless to attempt communication! Opinions expressed
during the last century were rather different, and
various schemes were put forward, ranging from
the sober to the frankly hare-brained. One idea was
to dig huge ditches in the Sahara, arranging the
pattern to make up some obvious geometrical
figure, so that the Martians would see the signal
and reply by making a similar pattern in one of
their deserts. About 1840, Von Littrow, Director of
the Vienna Observatory, proposed to construct an
immense triangle of "luminous points", either by
using reflected sun-rays or by means of artificial
lamps, so that Martian and lunar astronomers
would take the hint and reply suitably. Then, too,
there was Charles Cros, a Frenchman who achieved
some notoriety in the 1870s. Cros proposed to build
a large mirror, capable of focusing the Sun's heat
on to Mars, and fusing sand there in the manner of
a tremendous burning-glass; by moving the mirror
around, Cros claimed, it should be possible to write
words in the Martian deserts. He did not specify
what words he proposed to write—and I have often
wondered at our own reactions if mysterious words
started to appear in the Sahara, burned in the sand
by inquisitive Martians!

The arrival of radio communication produced a

crop of new ideas, and it is on record that in its early days the G.P.O. in London accepted a telegram sent to a Martian address, though it was dispatched with the prudent qualification: "Delivery not guaranteed". There was also the case of Madame Guzman, of Pau, who bequeathed a legacy of 100,000 francs to the Académie des Sciences, to be given to the first person who should discover the means of communication between the Earth and another world. In the terms of the bequest, Mars was specifically excluded, because Madame Guzman considered that the task would be too easy.

Even today there are various strange societies which continue to call up Mars by radio, or which claim to have established telepathic links with beings on planets out as far as Saturn.[1] And only a few years ago, a very eminent Russian astronomer, Iosif Shklovsky, put forward the hypothesis that the two dwarf satellites of Mars, Phobos and Deimos, are probably in the nature of space-stations, constructed by the Martians for reasons of their own. The idea of civilization on the Red Planet dies hard.

Lowly life-forms are notoriously hardy, and we cannot rule them out on any but the most hostile worlds. Unfortunately the Moon, which is so conveniently near at hand, fails upon every count. It is virtually without atmosphere, totally without

---

[1] Not long ago I attended such a meeting in London, during which the chief speaker relayed a long message from his "control", who was apparently floating somewhere in the far reaches of the Solar System. When the "control" announced that he had full command of all Earthly languages, I was ill-natured enough to ask a question in Norwegian. This proved quite defeating, as did French. Finally I was reduced to putting the question in English, but by then I was apparently somewhat unpopular, and I never received a satisfactory answer to my earnest inquiry.

liquid water, and without any protection from the various harmful radiations pouring in from space. We can hardly believe that any sort of living organism can survive there.

Lunar probes have already been dispatched, and it cannot be long now before samples of the soil are analyzed—either on the spot, by automatic equipment, or in our Earth laboratories after having been collected and brought home. The prospects of recovering a probe from the Moon are very good, and I shall be surprised if it is not accomplished within the next decade, whether or not manned landings are made by then. The chances of finding any living lunar organisms are, in my view, nil. Yet it is worth pausing for a moment to consider whether there may be evidence of past life.

The Earth is about 4,700 million years old, and the Moon must be of the same age. We may assume that life on Earth started to develop as soon as conditions became tolerable, and it is reasonable to think that the same could have happened on the Moon, though

The surface of the Moon photographed by the Russian probe *Luna 13* after a soft landing in 1967

the leaking-away of the atmosphere meant that instead of evolving, life there simply died out. It is not inconceivable that the lunar samples will contain traces of long-extinct organisms; in fact, primitive fossils. But I very much doubt whether conditions on the Moon ever became suitable for life, and we must also remember that there is no evidence that an Earth-type atmosphere was ever produced. Therefore, I suggest that the lunar world has always been sterile, and will remain so until the arrival of the first living creatures from Earth.

There is little point in speculating about Venus, because our knowledge is still too sketchy. A temperature of +500°F. does not sound at all promising, and any life there must be of a most elementary kind. But Mars is a more fruitful field, and serious efforts to clear up the problem of possible Martian life are bound to be made in the near future.

Ingenious devices have been planned, and may well work. For example, a rocket may land on the surface and then send out a "grab", either of the shovel or drill type, on the lines of an anteater's tongue, sticky enough to draw samples back into the rocket for examination. It is technically possible to carry out an analysis and transmit the results back home, and the worst problem is that of making a soft landing in the first instance, but this will no doubt be overcome, as it already has been in the case of Venus. Well before 1980, we ought to know whether Mars is a living world, using the term in a broad sense, or whether it is as sterile as the Moon. I still favour the first alternative, but I admit that *Mariner IV* has made me less confident than I used to be.

Beyond Mars? There are the asteroids, of course,

and the giant planets; we need waste no time on the innermost member of the Sun's family, Mercury, which is just as unfriendly as the Moon. With the asteroids, much depends upon whether or not they once made up a single, much larger body. All the asteroids put together would not make up a planet equal in size to the Moon, and it does not seem that such a small world, moving round the Sun at a considerable distance, would be suitable for the development of life, but we must also include the meteoritic bodies, and there have been periodical suggestions that some meteorites may contain traces of past life.

Most people have seen shooting-stars, which are tiny particles smaller than grains of sand, dashing into the Earth's air and being destroyed by frictional heating against the atmospheric particles. Meteors, to give them their correct name, tend to move round the Sun in shoals, so that each time the Earth passes through a shoal it collects a large number of shooting-stars. This happens many times in each year; the most spectacular shower, that of the Perseids, occurs during the early part of August. More rarely, a spectacular display is seen in mid-November. These Leonid meteors gave their last great display in 1966, when for several hours the sky as seen from some parts of the world, notably Arizona, seemed to be ablaze with shooting-stars. The display was missed in Europe, because it occurred around noon, and was over by the time that darkness fell.

Meteors burn themselves out at heights of over 40 miles, but now and then the Earth encounters a larger body, which can survive the complete drop to the ground without being destroyed and is then called a meteorite. For many years, scientists found it impossible to believe in "stones from heaven", but the question was finally settled on 26 April 1803, when a shower of stones fell at the French village of L'Aigle and was studied by a leading astronomer, Jean-Baptiste Biot. It was then established that there had been well-authenticated meteorite falls in earlier times; for instance, the Roman writer Livy had described a shower of rocks which had fallen on the Alban Hill in 654 B.C., and another early meteorite proved to be a mass of rock "the size of two millstones" which landed at Ægospotamos, in Greece, in 468 B.C. The Sacred Stone at Mecca is also a meteorite.

Many specimens are now known, and most museums have collections of them. The last British fall occurred at Barwell, in Leicestershire, on Christmas Eve 1965, causing both interest and alarm. The plate shows a fragment of it which I collected from a field when I went to the site some weeks later. Altogether, the Barwell Meteorite must have weighed about 200 lbs. before it broke up during its final descent through the atmosphere.

There are no reliable reports of anyone having been killed by a meteorite, because major falls are extremely rare. The famous Coon Butte Crater in Arizona is certainly of meteoritic origin, and there is a 60-ton meteorite still lying where it came down at Hoba West, in Africa; but both these falls were prehistoric. In our own time there have been only two really large meteorites, those of 1908 and 1947, both of which hit uninhabited areas of Siberia.

Meteorites seem to be close relatives of the asteroids, and are distinct from the tiny grain-sized meteors. If the asteroids were produced by the

Part of the Barwell meteorite, found in January 1966 after the fall of 24 December 1965. Weighing 2½ lbs., the fragment is shown here with a pipe for comparison

break-up of a larger planet, then so were the meteorites—and we may therefore be able to study pieces of a world that no longer exists.

The Arizona meteor crater, ¾ mile in diameter, made by a
prehistoric impact

In 1961, three American scientists published a
remarkable paper. They had been studying certain
rather unusual meteorites, notably one that had
fallen at Orgueil in France almost a century earlier,
and had come to the conclusion that certain "organized elements" were the remains of living
things. There can be no chance that life, however
lowly, can have evolved on anything so small as a
meteorite, so that if the claims were valid we would
have proof that the old, long-shattered planet had
been a living world.

Arguments raged for some years, but gradually it
became clear that the features observed in the
meteorites were not genuinely associated with
them, and that the "organized elements" were due
to Earth contamination introduced after the
meteorites had landed. This is now the accepted
view, disappointing though it may be. All in all, we

have to admit that there is no evidence of life elsewhere in the Solar System, either past or present,
apart possibly from a certain amount of primitive
vegetation on Mars.

Before turning to possible alien forms, something
ought to be said about another problem which is
being taken very seriously by space researchers.
This concerns the possible contamination of other
planets by organisms sent there from the Earth.

Bacteria and other familiar organisms are suited
to our own particular environment, and we do not
know whether they could survive elsewhere. The
chances of their being able to exist upon an airless
world such as the Moon are certainly very low, but
both Mars and Venus have atmospheres, and we
cannot be sure that terrestrial bacteria would not
thrive there if they were introduced. They might
even spread in runaway fashion, so that the whole
planet would be affected in a matter of days or
weeks.

From a moral viewpoint this does not matter
greatly, provided that there is no fear of our damag-
ing higher life-forms—and let us repeat that we can
virtually rule out any advanced life on either
Venus or Mars. Scientifically, however, the damage
would be irreparable. Future explorers would be
quite unable to work out which organisms were due
to Earth contamination, and which—if any—
belonged to the planet itself. The opportunity of
studying another world in its mint condition, so to
speak, would be lost forever.

With Venus, it may have been lost even now.
In 1966 the Russian probe *Venus 4* landed there, as
we have noted, and it is possible that contamination
has been introduced. Personally, I am not at all

pessimistic, partly because I doubt whether any bacteria carried on board the probe would survive on Venus, and partly because I have great faith in the efficiency of the Soviet decontamination methods, but one can never be 100 per cent sure; and if rockets of the 1970s and 1980s do indicate minute traces of organic material in the atmosphere of Venus, we shall never be certain whether or not it originated in the U.S.S.R.

Various methods of sterilization are employed, most of which involve exposing the probe to lethal gases or else to intensive radiation bombardment. It is likely that these methods are more than 95 per cent effective, and perhaps over 99 per cent, but the risk remains. It will always remain, and we have a clear-cut choice. Either we take the chance of introducing contamination, or else we abandon the whole idea of carrying out landings on worlds that have atmospheres. The second course is a negative one, and so we have no alternative but to make the decontamination as effective as possible and then trust to luck.

When the Russian vehicle hit Venus there was severe criticism from various eminent and influential scientists. No doubt this was understandable, but the overall problem remains, and sooner or later the choice would have had to be made in any case. It might have been wiser to wait until sterilization methods had been made more foolproof, but this too would have had its drawbacks.

Lunar vehicles are sterilized, but probably more on principle than because of any general belief in the contamination risk, since not even the hardiest of bacteria can be given much chance of survival on the Moon. It is with Mars that the main problems arise, because Mars is the only planet in the Solar System, beyond the Earth, where there is a reasonable chance of finding indigenous life. In the near future it will be practicable to soft-land an automatic probe there. Whether the planners would be justified in holding back because of the contamination risk is a debatable point. I rather think not, but I am quite ready to be converted.

Following up this theme, we must consider the possibilities of a probe returning from another world bringing back bacteria which would be harmful to ourselves. This was the "twist" in the plot of H. G. Wells' classic novel *The War of the Worlds*, written many years ago, in which monsters from Mars invade the Earth, mow down all opposition by means of their heat-rays and other weapons, and are wiped out only because they cannot withstand the bacteria which exist on Earth but which are absent from Mars. The implied warning must be taken very much to heart, because a single mistake might be disastrous. I would say that the chances of our importing any harmful bacteria from Mars are about one in a million, but they are not zero, and the greatest care will have to be taken. When it becomes possible to bring a probe back from Mars, it will presumably be put into an orbit round the Earth while it is scrupulously examined and decontaminated.

Again, can we be absolutely certain that such precautions will be effective? Obviously, the answer is "no". There may well be a pressure-group among scientists urging that no such experiment should be undertaken at all, and we can only await the results of further research before trying to make a decision. For any human being considered as a separate entity, the risk would be justifiable; there is much more danger in crossing Piccadilly Circus or Times Square in the rush-hour. But when the whole of humanity is involved, the responsibility of the planners is immense.

So far we have considered only life of the sort we can understand, and which is made up of living material based upon the element carbon. Novelists delight in going further, and describing alien forms quite beyond our scientific experience and which we might not even recognize as being intelligent. Ideas of this nature sound far-fetched enough, but they are not rejected by all serious scientists, so that they must be considered here.

Let us take Jupiter as a test case. There is no solid surface, so far as we can tell; there is no free oxygen in the atmosphere, and the surface temperature is very low indeed. The chemistry of any life-form on (or in) Jupiter would have to be alien in every sense of the term, and it has been suggested that a Jovian organism would probably be a sort of living balloon, floating in the dense gas. If it rose too high, it would become too cold for survival; if it sank too low, it would enter a region where the pressure, and perhaps the increased temperature, would destroy it. Our telescopes could show no traces of it, and it might avoid detection even with sampling probes of the future.

I have no personal faith in anything of the kind, and I would be very surprised to learn that there could be any sort of living material on Jupiter or the other giant planets. In fact, it seems that we are speculating unjustifiably; we have no proof that alien life-forms exist, and what evidence we have points in the other direction, though admittedly it is not conclusive. Jupiter is so far off, and has such a strong gravitational pull, that even by the technological standards of A.D. 2000 it is bound to be very difficult to send a probe there and keep control of its movements. (Bringing it back would be harder still, because of Jupiter's high escape velocity of 37 miles per second; tremendous power would be needed.) No doubt a Jupiter probe will be dispatched within the next few decades, but its purpose will be to investigate the nature of the planet and its surroundings, not to indulge in a search for life which is almost sure to prove abortive.

If we allow our imaginations to run riot, and suppose that we did in fact find evidence of an alien life-form, our attitude to it would have to be very carefully considered. There seems to be a general tendency to regard all extra-terrestrial life as potentially hostile and destructive, and this may be due in part to the pattern set by Wells' novel, which has had countless imitators. Yet I see no reason for any such attitude; if alien creatures exist, there may be grounds for supposing that they are superior to ourselves, and indeed it might be they who would regard *homo sapiens* as evil.

One's personal views are bound to colour any discussions of this sort, and I am making no attempt to be unbiased; I do not believe in alien life, on Jupiter or anywhere else, and I decline to change my opinions until or unless any fresh evidence comes to light. But there can be little doubt that extra-terrestrial life does exist in other Solar Systems, and we must now see what may be our chances of contacting it. We can forget about rocketry, because even a probe moving at the velocity of light would take years to achieve a round trip to any star. Excluding thought-travel and similar ideas, we must pin our hopes on radio.

At their velocity of 186,000 miles per second, radio waves are not fast enough to be satisfying, but nothing can outstrip them, so that we must make the best of the situation. Our only course is to select some suitable wavelength, and then see whether we can track down any signals from afar which appear to be artificial. This was the procedure followed by some American radio astronomers in 1960, in a project which had the code name of Ozma. A large radio telescope was used, and attention was concentrated upon radiations at a wavelength of 21 centimetres. This happens to be the wavelength of radiations sent out by clouds of hydrogen spread between the stars, and it was reasoned, quite logically, that any other radio astronomers, wherever they might be, would also tend to concentrate upon this particular wavelength.

The experiment went on for several months, but the results were predictably negative, and nothing more has been done in the United States. Later there came a sensational report that two Russian experimenters had detected artificial signals from a "super-civilization" millions of light-years away. The report was quite unfounded, and was hastily quashed by the Soviet Academy of Sciences, but at least it drove political crises and war news out of the newspaper headlines for a complete day!

To attempt to work out anything in the nature of an interplanetary communications code is somewhat futile. It could probably be done, by making use of mathematical symbols; after all, mathematics is universal, and we did not invent it—we merely discovered it. But even if we could identify

signals from another Solar System, the time-lag
would be crippling. With a planet at a distance of,
say, 11 light-years, a signal received in 1968 would
actually have been transmitted in 1957, and our
reply would not reach its destination until 1979,
making quick-fire repartee somewhat difficult.
Also, the chances of there being another advanced
civilization within several tens of light-years of us
are not very high. We have to look for a civilization
which has reached our own stage of development in
our own time. It is worth noting that if signals had
been intensively beamed to us as recently as fifty
years ago, we would have had no chance of detecting
them, because our equipment at that period was
too primitive. A rhythmical pattern of signals is as
much as we can ever hope for, even though this
alone would be sufficient to cause a radical change
in our outlook.

   Again we must remember that we are bound to be
out of date. If we could pick up signals from a
planet moving round the star Rigel, at a distance of
900 light-years from Earth, all we could prove would
be that civilization had existed there 900 years ago,
at the time of the Norman Conquest. (This may be a
bad example, because Rigel does not seem a suitable
star to have a planetary system, and in any case it
is too much to expect that our range of reception
could extend for as much as 900 light-years; but the
principles hold good.) And if we transmit signals
this year, on our selected wavelength of 21 centimetres, they might theoretically be received on
Rigel in the year 2868 or thereabouts. By then,
humanity may have evolved into something very
splendid and enlightened—but it is also possible
that the Earth will be an uninhabited, radioactive

waste, and our potential listeners on their planet circling Rigel will have no means of knowing. Neither could they find out quickly, since a reply signal from them would not reach Earth until about A.D. 3768.

To sum up: even if further experiments on the Ozma line are carried out in the coming years, as is quite likely, they can never do more than tell us that other intelligences exist. By radio, two-way communication in any understandable form is a hopeless proposition. Yet nothing can move more quickly than a radio wave.

Earlier in this chapter I referred to thought-propagation. I did so briefly and rather scornfully, because as yet our knowledge of thought-communication is virtually nil; there have been many experiments with telepathy, but to say that the results are inconclusive is to put it mildly. Even so, it seems that something of the sort is the only chance for future full contacts with other intelligent races, assuming of course that there is no startling break-through in the more conventionally scientific field. At present we know so little that any speculation is pointless, but if mankind survives until the thirtieth century, and maintains the rate of progress that we have achieved since about 1900, things may be different. It may be a slender hope, but it is better than nothing at all; and we may be sure that so long as we keep our interest in the universe, our search for "other men" will go on.

Rockets in Peace and War

HAD THERE BEEN no war in 1939, there would be no Moon-rockets today. Amateurs would still be experimenting within the limits and rules and regulations laid down by the Explosives Act of 1875; by now, some modest high-altitude vehicles would have been sent aloft, but that would have been all. The development of massive space-probes has been possible only because much of the research has a military slant.

Nobody in their senses would suggest that the 1939 war, or indeed any war, has its bright side simply because it leads to scientific advance. It is a tragedy that astronautics and warfare have been linked, but the facts speak for themselves, and all we can do now is to see whether there is any hope of stopping further trends in the same unpalatable direction.

The rocket has a long history as a war-weapon. It was certainly used in a battle between the Chinese and the Mongols in 1232, and now and then it was employed in Europe through the next few centuries; during the Napoleonic period, Britain had its rocket mounted corps, and of course the famous line about

192

"the rockets' red glare" in the American anthem was written immediately after a British attack on Fort McHenry in 1813. So far as is known, old-fashioned war rockets were last used by the Russians just before 1880. These powder rockets vanished from the military scene because they were no match for conventional artillery; between 1880 and 1944 the only practical use for rockets was in launching scientific equipment to modest heights, and in sending lifelines between the shore and ships in distress.

There is all the difference in the world between nineteenth-century war rockets, which exploded and were capable of killing one or two enemy soldiers, and modern rocket missiles, which can be equipped with nuclear warheads capable of wiping out whole cities (and, if used on a grand scale, wiping out civilization). It is a regrettable but inescapable fact that a launcher able to send a probe to the Moon or Mars can also, with relatively minor modifications, send a nuclear bomb to any part of the Earth.

Before discussing rockets of this nature, it is as well to pause and mention various other military applications of space research. For instance, there was the American "West Ford" experiment, in which large numbers of tiny copper needles were sent up and spread round the Earth in a belt, the idea being to use this belt as a layer capable of reflecting certain kinds of radio waves and thereby providing a reliable link in time of war. The method might work quite well, and would even be more consistent than the natural reflecting layers, which are always liable to be upset by activity on the Sun. On the other hand, a permanent needle-belt would completely ruin some branches of radio astronomy, and it is not surprising that scientists all over the world protested volubly. Naturally, their protests were ignored, and the needles were dispatched. The first launching failed; the second achieved its object, though mercifully the needle belt subsequently dispersed and no lasting damage was done.

To wreck radio astronomy would be a scientific disaster, but the second American military experiment, that of exploding a nuclear device in the upper atmosphere, was much more dangerous. It was meant to cause a temporary disruption of the natural radiation zone, and to create a new one. There is no doubt in my mind that this was the most irresponsible scientific experiment ever undertaken. It is true that no permanent harm resulted, but I suspect that this was due to sheer good luck.

To stifle the accusation of being anti-American (which I certainly am not), let me add that the conventional nuclear testing by Britain and Russia is just as bad, and in the long run may be worse, since the effects of contamination are cumulative. The lesson behind all this, of course, is that there is no present-day Government adult enough to be entrusted with dangerous scientific weapons, and that sooner or later there will be either an accident or else a fatal misunderstanding. The situation today is different from anything previously experienced. Before the nuclear age, a war could be fought with little danger to non-combatants, but nowadays everybody is involved. It is by no means impossible that, say, an Esquimau living in the Arctic during the 1970s may end his days by dying of radiation poisoning released after a dispute between statesmen in Washington, Moscow and Pekin.

This is one side of the picture, but there is another. Few politicians have any technical knowledge of science; if they had, then they would not be politicians. I remember a profound statement made in 1954 by Lord (then Mr. Clement) Attlee, in which he said that "our whole civilization is at stake . . . the danger comes from the scientists". Though Mr. Attlee made his statement on April the First, which under the circumstances was rather an appropriate day, he did unconsciously pinpoint the root of the trouble. No political leader can handle a scientific weapon unless a scientific team gives it to him. And surely the main hope for the future lies with scientists, who could remove the danger simply by declining to hand over dangerous toys to people not responsible enough to have control of them. There is a distinct analogy with the man who takes a group of children into a shed full of dry wood and leaves them there with a box of matches.

I think, and hope, that most scientists would share this view, but under the present uneasy world situation each nation is afraid to take the lead. An American nuclear physicist who withheld information which might lead to an even more destructive bomb would be classed as a traitor, and so would his British, Russian, Chinese, and of course German counterparts. Therefore, the children are kept fully supplied with their matches.

All this is bound up closely with the progress of rocket research. The rockets themselves are harmless; the peril lies in the warheads they carry. This is why the American and Russian space programmes, which at present are the only ones that matter, are totally independent. The amount of duplicated research, with corresponding waste of time and money, is quite staggering—though but for the military aspect the research would not have been financed in the first place.

Were it possible for the United States and Soviet projects to be combined, plus certain aspects in which Britain leads the way, the Moon would soon be within reach. It would cost money, but the expenditure would be justified, for reasons I propose to give later in the present book. Certainly the cost would be in no way comparable with the amounts now being squandered daily upon weapons. Stripped of their armaments bills, the great nations would have plenty of cash to spare.

It has been claimed that too much attention is being given to the man-in-space project, and too little to unmanned rockets. There may be some truth in this, and prestige certainly enters into it, but the overall programmes are so closely inter- twined that it is futile to try to separate them. When we consider space research itself, we must agree that the military aspects are very slight, and are confined chiefly to reconnaissance, since it is easy enough to send a satellite on a spy mission over hostile territory (as is done regularly). The idea of setting up a space-station, poised ready to rain down nuclear bombs on enemy cities, is absurd for many reasons. If mankind really wants to destroy itself, it can do so quickly enough by using ground-to-ground nuclear missiles. Indeed, suffi- cient missiles already exist, which is a frightening thought when we remember the mentalities of the people who control them.

One idea, current not long ago, was that of a space-mirror, to be put into orbit and used to focus the Sun's rays on to the ground below, thereby reducing an enemy city to a smouldering ruin. A recent modification, from America, was to set up a huge mirror over Vietnam and light up the jungles at night. However, it seems that even if such a mirror could be constructed and orbited, it could be destroyed by a suitably guided missile, and there seems no chance that anything will come of the scheme.

In the 1950s it was also thought by some writers that any nation which could control the Moon could also control the Earth. I have never been sure just how this principle was meant to work. If successful lunar rockets were confined to one nation (logically, either the United States or the Soviet Union), then there might be a temporary monopoly of the Moon, and in fact this could still happen. Yet the military advantages would be negligible. The fact that the successful nation would presumably have taken the lead in rocketry as a whole is naturally relevant, but has nothing directly to do with the Moon. I only hope that the first lunar bases will be international ones, though I confess that the wish is father to the thought.

What must be realized is that there is no chance whatsoever of turning the Moon into a flourishing colony. It is so hostile that its population must always be sparse, and in our time, at least, the most we can expect is a collection of isolated research bases. The prospect of any one country "claiming the Moon" does not arise. Suppose, for instance, that the Earth were uninhabited, and that some alien race managed to establish small bases on the sites of London, New York and Sydney? The aliens could hardly lay claim to the whole of the globe—at least, not logically.

So far as lunar bases are concerned, we have the precedent of Antarctica, which is the one really encouraging piece of development in the field of international exploration. Antarctica is not a friendly continent, and its population is confined to various research establishments set up by different nations, all of which are pleasingly remote from the centres of political intrigue, and which can therefore carry out their work in peace. If we ever reach the stage of being able to supply a sizable lunar colony, we shall presumably have passed beyond the stage of wanting to put bombs in our rockets.

Recently there has been considerable discussion about what has become known as space law, in which attempts have been made to lay down international codes of behaviour for use "beyond the Earth". Frankly, I can think of no greater waste of time. Once the Earth has been left behind, common sense will have to be the deciding factor; if this is ignored, the results are sure to be tragic.

All being well, international co-operation in space will be achieved eventually, but there is always the risk that rocket weapons will be diverted back to warfare before mankind has become mentally adult. And at the risk of going outside my main theme, it seems only right to make some further comments about nuclear-headed rockets, the most destructive of all weapons.

Much is heard of the so-called nuclear deterrent. It is claimed that in any major war ahead of us nuclear bombs will not be used, because they will damage the attacker as grievously as the intended victim. Comparisons are drawn with poison gas, which was used in the 1914 war and not (officially) in the 1939 war. There are evident weaknesses in both arguments, and, to take them in the reverse order, we can at once dispose of the poison gas analogy; gas was not extensively used between 1939 and 1945 not because of any moral scruples, but because it was hopelessly ineffective in modern war. And to suppose that nuclear weapons will be ignored in a future clash is quite absurd. Of course the weapons would be used—not perhaps at first, but eventually, because the leaders of a nation on the brink of defeat will have nothing left to lose, and will clutch at any forlorn chance of snatching a dramatic victory at the last moment.

This is not intended to be a plea for unilateral nuclear disarmament, and the present-day nuclear disarmers, with their beards and banners, are reasoning along very different lines. But the situation does exist in which rockets could be used to even worse effect than has been the case in past years.

Unless scientists of all nations—I repeat, *all* nations—are ready to call a halt, and withhold their matches, there is no obvious solution; and the chances of an effective declaration of this kind are, unfortunately, negligible. All we can hope is to stagger along from crisis to crisis until a saner attitude prevails.

The one real hope would be the development of a widely-accepted religion in which the use of force between nations would be unthinkable under any circumstances. This may eventually be the answer, but as yet there are no signs of it. I have no idea of what form such a religion might take; but I very much doubt whether it would authorize its officials to bless soldiers about to kill other soldiers, airmen ready to drop bombs on enemy cities, or technicians preparing their nuclear rockets. I only hope that we find it in time.

[4]

Explorers of the Future

WE HAVE LOOKED at the sombre side of rocket research. Now let us turn to what may happen if common-sense prevails, and let us also assume that it becomes possible to devote considerable time and money to space matters without neglecting urgent needs at home. As I have stressed several times in this book, there would be no difficulty here but for the crippling armaments bills.

The first major development will be the exploration of the Moon. We can to all intents and purposes rule out the hope of finding life there, either past or present, and the immediate need will be to see whether there are any materials that will be of practical help. In particular, it has been suggested that ice may exist below ground level. I have serious doubts about this, because it seems to me that the lunar landscape is likely to be a barren, volcanic waste which will give us no assistance at all, but I may be wrong.

A scientific base will presumably be set up as soon as manned lunar flight becomes relatively easy. This base will be permanently manned, but the crews will have to be changed at regular intervals;

the time of a continuous spell of duty will have to be calculated according to what we learn about radiation hazards, reduced gravity and so forth. Perhaps the feeble gravity will be the limiting factor. It may sound very pleasant to a 14-stone astronaut to learn that on the Moon he will weigh less than 3 stone, and he will seem remarkably powerful—but he will eventually return to Earth, and muscles weakened by lunar conditions may prove inadequate. Time will tell; but it is not likely that any Earthman could stay on the Moon for a period of years and then come back unaffected.

The design of a Lunar Base has been the subject of innumerable drawings, plans and written descriptions. The most attractive pattern is that of a hemispherical dome, kept inflated by the pressure of the air inside it, and resembling a huge bubble on the Moon's surface. This is all very well, but we must not forget meteoroids and radiation problems, and it may eventually be necessary to "go underground", either by using natural caves or by making artificial ones.

On the lunar equator the temperature extremes are unpleasantly great, and range from over +200°F. down to below −250°F. This will not affect the explorers, who will in any case have to wear full space-suits as soon as they leave the shelter of their rocket or their Base, but great changes of temperature do influence certain inanimate substances, and there are various materials that will have to be avoided in the construction of the Base. This is the sort of unfamiliar detail that space-planners will never be able to ignore. Away from the equator the midday heat will be less, but there is no avoiding the bitter cold of lunar night.

Transport and communications give us problems of their own. The Moon's surface is undoubtedly rough, and in places probably unsafe. Hermann Oberth, the Roumanian mathematician whose book of the 1920s really brought astronautics into the public eye, has gone so far as to design a moon-car which can hop over hazards such as pits and cracks, but all we can really say as yet is that our normal vehicles will have to be drastically modified and toughened for lunar use.

The only possible method of communication is by radio, since there can be no sound upon an airless world such as the Moon (once outside the Base, of course). Normally, radio range will be limited to the distance of the horizon, but even this will be a matter of less than two miles, because the Moon is a small globe and has a sharply-curving surface, and there are no high-altitude layers to reflect radio waves back to the ground. Tall masts may improve things somewhat; but for linking up one research base with another, different techniques will have to be employed.

On the Earth-turned hemisphere of the Moon, radio messages could be relayed from one part of the lunar surface to another simply by routing them via the Earth, but this will be both tricky and cumbersome, and it may be more practicable to set up a chain of communications satellites to circle the Moon and act as relays. Following the unhappy West Ford experiment with space-needles, described in the last chapter, I did publish a suggestion that some such belt might be set up round the Moon; but here too there might be objections from radio astronomers (to whom the Moon will be a paradise), and communications satellites of the

Early Bird or Telstar type will probably provide a better answer.

Certainly the view from the Moon will be "unearthly" in every sense of the word. The sky will be black even during the daytime, because there is no air to scatter the sunlight; the Earth will be a brilliant globe, remaining to all intents and purposes stationary in the sky, but showing a complete cycle of phases from new to full and then back to new once more. The stars will not twinkle, but will be steely and clear-cut. One trouble may be the harsh light; there can be no soft half-shades, and the astronauts' eyes will have to be carefully protected.

From the averted side of the Moon, of course, the Earth will never be seen, since it will remain below the horizon all the time. Otherwise the sky will have much the same aspect, and day and night conditions will be the same as on the Earth-turned side—except, of course, that the nights will be much darker, because of the absence of earthlight.

Another bright suggestion is that the Moon may contain valuable minerals or other substances, which could be brought home to Earth on a purely commercial basis. To me, this seems remarkably unlikely. If the Moon's surface is volcanic, there may well be minerals which we class as rare, and there will be meteoric débris too; but to transport it would be hopelessly costly. However, research samples will be of the utmost scientific value, since they will tell us more not only about the past story of the Moon, but about the early period of the Solar System. Before the first manned landings, we should know more or less what to expect, because samples will have been collected and brought back by unmanned probes. The American authorities have already started to set up a special laboratory to deal with lunar materials, and no doubt the Russians are making preparations of their own.

Religious objections to space-travel have been voiced, on the grounds that we were created on Earth and are presumably meant to stay there. One well-known author—C. S. Lewis, who wrote three science-fiction novels in which he produced some splendid Martian bug-eyed monsters—went so far as to call the great distances within the Solar System "God's quarantine regulations". I am not clear as to who is meant to be quarantined from whom; but it does not seem that there is much essential difference between going to an uninhabited world, such as the Moon, and an unhabited continent, such as Antarctica. Indeed, from Lewis' point of view the Moon might even be preferable, since there are no penguins to have their lives upset!

The second point about the overall projects is a much more serious one. Any chance of relieving the Earth's over-population problem by transferring the surplus to the Moon, Mars or anywhere else is absolutely out of the question, because of the numbers of people involved. Eventually, if all goes well, it is not impossible that the Moon may support a colony of a million people. (I regard this as a gross over-estimate, but let us take an extreme case.) Clearly, this would make no perceptible difference to the overcrowding situation; it would be rather like trying to solve London's traffic problem by banning all cars coming in daily from, say, Tunbridge Wells.

There can be no doubt that apart from the risk of nuclear war, the problem of ever-increasing numbers is the greatest crisis that humanity has to face. It is not a new realization; it was pointed out as long ago as 1796 by the Rev. Robert Malthus, whose essay on "The Principle of Population as it Affects Future Improvement of Society" caused such a stir in intellectual and religious circles. Malthus stressed that human society cannot exist indefinitely unless its numbers are controlled, and there must be a definite limit. He pointed out that quite apart from the positive checks of war and disease, moral restraint is necessary if the situation is not to become out of hand. Much of what he wrote is only too valid today, even though the crisis is much nearer than he could have foreseen.

The Earth can support only a set number of people. Its living-room is not infinite, and neither are its natural resources. If there are no more destructive wars, and if medical science can deal with any potential epidemics, over-population will become really serious well before the end of the twenty-second century, if not before. Instead of trying to increase the birth-rate, every Government should now be considering possible ways of reducing it, but unfortunately nobody has any idea of what method can be adopted. Malthus' "moral restraint" does not work, the attitude of at least some of the great world religions is frankly stupid, and we are all doing our best to ignore the whole matter, with the result that we are storing up a terrible legacy for our great-great-grandchildren. Whether positive action will be taken in time remains to be seen. It is not my purpose here to delve deeply into such matters, particularly as I can make no useful contribution; all I am stressing is that so far as over-population is concerned, lunar and planetary colonization cannot help.

Martian bases are the practical concern of our descendants, not of ourselves. The findings of America's probe Mariner IV, which showed Mars to be much more like the Moon than like the Earth, have caused a change in outlook; the pleasant, relatively flimsy Martian Base of our dreams has had to give way to something much more harsh and lunar, and it will certainly be impossible to go for a walk on Mars except with the protection of full vacuum-suiting. The atmosphere is appreciable, but not dense enough to be of immediate use.

Of course, there may be underground water supplies, and this will help considerably, since the voyage will last for months and a definite period will have to be spent on the planet. Moreover, it may be that certain types of Earth organisms will be persuaded to grow there, though admittedly the chances seem rather slim. The difficulties of the actual journey are so obvious that they need not be stressed here; our present technology is incapable of solving them, though by the 2060s, perhaps much earlier, it ought to be a different story.

Now that we know Mars to be crater-scarred, we must give up the idea of ordinary wheeled vehicles for travelling about the planet's surface, and we must await the results of transport on the Moon, bearing in mind that Martian conditions may be somewhat less rough. Up to 1965, it was confidently expected that conventional aircraft would be able to function there, at least at low levels, but this, too, now seems to be wrong, because the atmosphere is too thin. On the other hand, there may be reflecting layers dense enough to allow radio communication between one research base and another. One thing that could never be done in the open, incidentally, would be to use smoke signals. The air contains so little oxygen that it will be impossible to light a fire!

With Venus, we can say little as yet. If the surface temperature is around +500°F., landings there will not be easy—to put it mildly!—and preliminary investigations will have to be made by manned rockets of the fly-by variety, circling Venus at a respectful distance.

Of the other nearby worlds, Mercury can be counted out for the moment. It is just as hostile as the Moon, and even more inaccessible than Venus or Mars. Radiation hazards would certainly be severe, and a voyage to Mercury would be a difficult matter by any standards, so that within the next century or so we can hope for no more than un-manned probes.

Sending a rocket to an asteroid would be a rather more attractive proposition, and on-the-spot in-vestigations would be valuable. There would be very little gravity, and on a really small world an astro-naut who jumped upward would depart permanently into space—unless, of course, he had taken the precaution of using a safety-line.

Some years ago, an impressive-looking book pub-lished in America returned to the old idea that it might be possible to fit rocket motors to asteroids and guide them into desirable orbits. It was also suggested that an asteroid might be hollowed out and used as a natural interplanetary station, or even a holiday camp; if provided with an internal atmosphere it would make an excellent and most unusual resort! So far as the first idea is concerned, it must be said, with regret, that the authors can have had no idea of the forces that would be needed to alter the orbit of even a dwarf asteroid. And with regard to holiday resorts, I can only say that I have my doubts, even though it would be fascinating to watch one's next-door neighbour strolling in his garden above one's head.

Looking even further into the future, we come to the giant planets. Actual landings there will never be possible, but there is no reason against sending probes out to some of the satellites. Jupiter has four large attendants, and Saturn several, one of which (Titan) is known to have an atmosphere, though the composition of this atmosphere is chiefly methane and the temperature is very low.

Yet it is not likely that chemical-fuel rockets will ever prove equal to the task of sending a man out as far as Jupiter. The time taken for such a voyage would be hopelessly long, and a round trip would take an appreciable part of a lifetime. If the giants are ever to be reached, we must find a more efficient source of power. The solution may lie in what is termed the ion-rocket, in which atomic particles are expelled from the exhaust, giving a thrust which is admittedly low but which can be maintained almost indefinitely. At the moment, full-scale ion-rockets are theoretical only, but they should eventually be built.

From Pluto, outermost of the planets, the Sun would appear as nothing more than an intensely brilliant point. A Plutonian astronomer would have a poor view of the Solar System as a whole, and he could never see the Earth, which would be completely drowned in the rays of the Sun. Uranus and Neptune could be seen, though not prominently, but Saturn would be elusive; it is interesting to note that Pluto is much further away from Saturn than we are, though this is not always easy to grasp from a quick look at a plan of the Solar System.

Provided that we solve the nuclear war menace, the over-population crisis, and various technical problems that we cannot as yet define, I see no reason why men from Earth should not eventually travel out as far as Pluto. I very much doubt whether rockets, even of the ion variety, will take us any further, because at any practicable speeds it would take thousands or millions of years to reach the nearest star. We would need to move at near the speed of light to bring the time of travel down to a few years, and this leads us into fresh difficulties.

At speeds near 186,000 miles per second, strange things begin to happen with regard to both time and mass. For a body moving near optic velocity, time slows down. It has been calculated that if a spacecraft could leave Earth for the star Procyon ($10\frac{1}{2}$ light-years away) and move at 99·9% of the speed of light, it could make the round trip in 21 years of Earth-time; but to the crew of the rocket, the period would seem to be only 3 years, so that the astronauts would return home to find themselves "younger" than their nephews and nieces. The effect increases with still greater speeds, and when we reach the exact velocity of light it is found that time stands still. In other words, travel at optic velocity is theoretically impossible.

Fantastic though this time-dilation effect may seem, there is practical proof of it. The Earth is being constantly bombarded by high-velocity atomic particles known as cosmic rays, which smash into the upper air and create other particles which we call mu-mesons. Since these mu-mesons are formed at altitudes of ten miles and over, and last for only about one two-millionth of a second before disintegrating, they ought not to last for long enough to reach the surface of the Earth; yet many of them do—because they are travelling at near the velocity of light, and their time is slowed down relative to ours, so that they can survive until reaching ground level.

The time-dilation effect has been questioned now and then (it has been suggested that the time gained on the way out to a distant star would be lost again on the way back!) but it does appear to be valid. Moreover, there is another effect, according to which the mass of a body becomes theoretically infinite when optic velocity is reached. Luckily, these mass and time effects are quite negligible at velocities of the order we can attain, and for journeys inside the Solar System we can forget about them. It is only when we consider interstellar travel that they become significant.

Science-fiction writers are understandably fond of introducing space-warps, time-warps and other ingenious devices, which sound very convincing in a novel but are likely to remain there. The deep-freeze technique, in which the astronauts are kept in a state of suspended animation throughout their voyage and are woken up only when close to their target, is just as implausible. And little can be said in favour of the space-ark, in which the original travellers die on the outward journey, leaving children to continue the voyage and hoping that their remote descendants will survive to make what is graphically called "planetfall" across the Galaxy. No: if we are to achieve interstellar travel, it must be by some means about which we are still so ignorant that we cannot even speculate.

To launch an unmanned interstellar probe would be an amusing intellectual exercise, but nothing more, because it could not be guided for more than a very limited distance; it would have no set target; and it would pass out of all range at an early point in its journey, so that nobody would ever know what happened to it. There is always the slim chance that such a probe might some day be contacted by beings in another Solar System, and if the vehicle had been suitably stocked with contemporary material these beings might be able to draw up some sort of picture of the twentieth-century Earth; but as the probe could not possibly reach its target for several millions of years, the information would be rather dated. Moreover, the chances of the probe being found at all are negligible, and all things considered the experiment would seem rather a waste of time. I have often wondered at our reactions if a probe from afar landed on Earth, but I fear that such a thing will never happen.

Without wishing to end upon a flat note, I must again stress that all these varied schemes of lunar and Martian bases, probes to asteroids, and eventual contacts with the outer planets depend upon our not encountering any major hazard which could upset all our plans. The weak link may be the human body, and it is always possible that the frailties of human physique will rule out any long journeys, in which case our personal exploration would be limited to the Moon. I am far from pessimistic, and I do not consider that anything of the sort is likely, but we cannot yet be fully confident. Until our pioneer astronauts have landed successfully on the Moon, we cannot say how much further the men of the future will be able to go.

[5]

Other Men

LOGIC TELLS US that we are alone in the Solar System, but not alone in the universe. The number of other civilizations must be staggeringly great, even if we exclude alien life-forms of the bug-eyed monster variety. And since we have no hope of getting in touch with any distant race, at least by our present techniques, we can only make guesses as to what they may be like.

Let us first consider a star similar to the Sun, which, as we know, is very run-of-the-mill in our Galaxy. As a typical example, we may take Delta Pavonis in the constellation of the Peacock, which is easily visible to the naked eye even though it is too far south to be seen from Europe. It is 19 light-years from us, or over 100 million million miles; its mass is 98 per cent of that of the Sun, and its surface temperature is very much the same. There seems no valid reason why it should not have a planetary system, and it is reasonable to suppose that there may be a planet moving in the star's "ecosphere". The ecosphere is the region in which an Earth-like planet would be neither too hot nor too cold for life to exist. For the Sun, the limits of

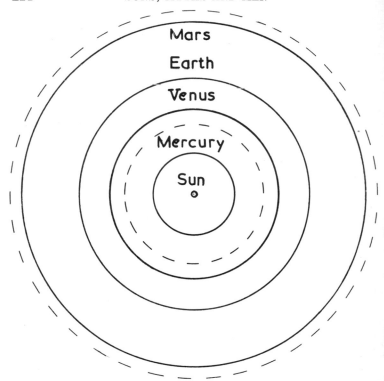

THE ECOSPHERE OF THE SUN. This diagram shows, to scale, the orbits of the four inner planets Mercury, Venus, Earth and Mars. The space between the two dashed circles indicates the ecosphere—the region in which the temperature is neither too hot nor too cold for life to exist, given a suitable planet. The ecosphere extends from within the orbit of Venus to slightly beyond the orbit of Mars. Therefore, Mercury lies outside the ecosphere, and must be regarded as hopelessly hot; Venus is on the "hot" side but still within the ecosphere; the Earth is ideally placed almost in the middle part of the ecosphere, and Mars lies uncomfortably close to the "cold" boundary. The next planet, Jupiter, is a long way beyond the ecosphere the ecosphere are probably about 60,000,000 and 150,000,000 miles, so that Venus lies near the inner boundary, Mars near the outer boundary, and the Earth just about in the middle. For Delta Pavonis, these distances would be reduced slightly, but not significantly.

We assume, then, an Earth-type planet moving round Delta Pavonis inside the star's ecosphere, giving an equable temperature. The planet is further assumed to have a terrestrial-style atmosphere, adequate water supplies, and a rotation period of the same order as ours. What sort of life may we expect there?

The only reference-point is the Earth, where we know a good deal about the evolution of life. Nature has discarded certain experiments, such as the dinosaurs, and has produced *homo sapiens*, each member of which has one head, two arms, two legs and a complex nerve-system. It is reasonable to think that we have developed along these lines simply because such a pattern is well suited to our environment. If the Earth had been more massive, the gravitational pull at the surface would have been stronger, and we should have had to be provided with sturdier frames; if the Earth had been less massive, then mankind would have been more flimsy.

In this case, it seems that our hypothetical beings on the planet of Delta Pavonis are likely to be very similar to ourselves, physically at least. No doubt they are not identical—but after all, an Esquimau is not identical physically with an African native or a European. On the world moving round Delta Pavonis, I, at least, would look for bipeds instantly recognizable as "men".

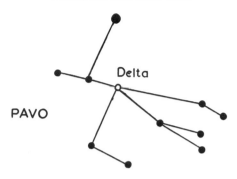

POSITION OF THE STAR DELTA PAVONIS. Pavo (the Peacock) is a fairly conspicuous constellation, but unfortunately it is too far south to be seen from Britain or the United States

One obviously important point is that of timescale. Because Delta Pavonis is similar to the Sun, it is probably about the same age, and its planets will be about as old as the Earth; that is to say, between 4,000 and 5,000 million years. Yet Man is a newcomer, and as recently as ten million years ago he had not appeared. Ten million years is not much when we are considering a total age of thousands of millions of years, and this is worth bearing in mind, because if we visited the planet of Delta Pavonis and found no advanced life there we would be most unwise in assuming that no intelligent life would ever develop; a further visit in a few million years' time might make all the difference. Similarly, a "Delta Pavonian" who had come to Earth during the Ice Age, which ended a mere 10,000 years ago, would have to come back again in order to satisfy himself that the primitive reindeer-hunters were capable of evolving into races able to build nuclear bombs, bacteriological weapons and other manifestations of modern civilization.

Of course, we have no proof of any planet attending Delta Pavonis. There may be no Solar System there, and in any case there may be no suitable planet moving within the ecosphere. Delta Pavonis was taken as an example only because it is one of the nearest stars of solar type; if the choice turns out to be bad, there are plenty of alternatives.

My opinion, which is personal only and may be very wide of the mark, is that a planet of roughly the size and mass of the Earth, moving within the ecosphere of a star similar to the Sun, is likely to produce life of strictly terrestrial type. If this argument is accepted, we are justified in speculating further, and seeing whether we can decide upon the course of events there.

The early history of a humanoid race depends entirely upon its environment, and upon local conditions in particular. Earthmen played no part in their development; they were concerned with survival, and it was inevitable that civilizations should arise from Stone Age beginnings. The fact that one tribe might attack and destroy another made no difference whatsoever to the overall picture. Even when the first great nations appeared, the picture was still fundamentally the same. Rome destroyed Carthage, and ploughed up its site; this was unfortunate for the Carthaginians, but it did not influence the course of human history except in that one particular area of the Mediterranean. Later, William of Normandy conquered Britain, and here too the results, profound though they were, were felt over only a limited region. If Napoleon had overrun England as well as the rest of Europe, I should still be seated at my desk typing out the manuscript of this book. It is only in our own era that a new sort of situation has arisen.

To repeat a little of what was said earlier: we have reached a truly crucial point, and a third world war now might result in the total destruction of mankind. The danger is due to weaknesses in our mental make-up. It might also affect beings on planets moving round other solar-type stars, and I strongly suspect that this is so, because these beings will probably be of the same kind as ourselves and will have the same failings. Under such circumstances, any small event may tip the scales. An ambitious dictator in one country; an incompetent and nervous government in another; the chance dropping of a practice bomb upon some vital territory—any of these might prove disastrous.

Looking on the brighter side, the critical period is not likely to last for very long. On Earth, it may be said to have begun in 1945, with the launching of the first atom-bomb. By 2145 it should be over, since we will have made enough mental progress to shoulder our responsibilities. In other words, we have to hope that we shall survive for the few centuries of our adolescence. The same should be true for other races, some of which will destroy themselves while others will not.

What, then, is happening today on the Earth-type planet of Delta Pavonis, if it exists? There could be a collection of Stone Age communities; there could be a mediæval world of warring nations; there could be a scientific civilization busying itself with building elementary space-ships and trying to find out something about the history of the universe. There might be either a dead planet, soaked in radioactivity from its final war, or else an enlightened civilization which has grown up safely and cast its armaments on to the scrap-heap. Any of these possibilities is quite logical, and it is a pity that we cannot find out which is correct.

Whether or not Delta Pavonis has a suitable planet, we may be sure that other suns have plenty, so that our Galaxy must contain hundreds of millions of "other Earths", and the same is true for all the other galaxies. Life is commonplace, and this realization is bound to affect our philosophy, provided that we are brave enough to think about it. The notion that our world can have been specially singled out for personal attention by an all-powerful God makes very little sense. To say this is not to adopt an atheistic attitude, and indeed the reverse is probably true.

The test of a civilization must lie in whether it can develop a suitable religion before or during its critical period, and this is what we have yet to do. The hackneyed argument that we have been divinely presented with the true religion, and are corrupting it because of our sinful tendencies, is somewhat puerile when examined closely, though it does provide a convenient escape-route for people who want to bury their heads in the metaphorical sand. I do not propose to persue the matter further, because the facts speak for themselves.

So much for civilizations that have grown up along our own lines in Earth-type environments. These may account for only a small percentage of the grand total, and it is worth making some guesses about races of quite different kind, but, as before, it seems pointless to speculate with regard to completely alien life-forms, the existence of which is highly dubious and about which we have no information whatsoever. It is more profitable to confine ourselves to life built upon our own pattern.

Solar-type stars may have planets inconveniently close to the inner or outer edges of their ecospheres, so that the environments would correspond to those of Venus and Mars respectively. A world near the inner boundary of the ecosphere might be habitable near its poles (assuming a suitable axial tilt) but too hot near its equator, though this would depend largely upon the land-and-sea distribution on the surface, and under such circumstances it is hardly likely that any advanced civilization would develop. Planets near the outer border of the ecosphere would be more Martian in temperature, but of course Mars itself would be reasonably welcoming if it were of greater mass and could retain a thicker atmosphere. I suggest that if Mars had been as massive as the Earth, it would have produced Martians.

Stars of non-solar type are not so promising as centres of planetary systems, but we cannot rule them out, and we know for certain that some dim red dwarfs have planet companions—Barnard's Star being the best example. With dwarfs, the ecospheres would be close-in, but would still be present even though the chances of life-bearing planets are clearly less. And for highly luminous stars, we run into time-scale difficulties. These stars evolve relatively quickly, and it is not very probable that complex life will have enough leisure to evolve upon any planets moving round brilliant giants, though again we cannot be sure.

The view from a planet moving round a red dwarf or a hot white giant would be remarkable. The dwarf would cast a dull, reddish glare; with the giant, the ecosphere would be so far out that the star would appear small but intensely bright. In a binary system, the effects would be even more spectacular, and we can profitably pause to glance at Alpha Centauri, the closest star in the sky apart from the Sun.

Alpha Centauri—alas, too far south to rise in Europe or North America—is a triple system, rather more than four light-years away from us. The faintest member of the trio, Proxima, is also the nearest to the Solar System, but is some way from the main pair, and is a red dwarf unlikely to be attended by a habitable planet. Of the bright components, one is slightly more massive and luminous than the Sun, while the other is decidedly cooler and fainter. The distance between the two ranges from about 1,000,000,000 miles to 3,300,000,000 miles, so that the stars are always at a distance from each other greater than that separating Saturn and our Sun. The revolution period around the common centre of gravity is 80 years.

It is clear that each star can have a proper ecosphere, and so either component may have a habitable planet. If so, these beings will have not only a conventional sun, but also a much smaller "second sun", which will frequently stay above the horizon at night-time and prevent any proper darkness. From Alpha Centauri, the Sun would appear as a distinctly unremarkable star in the constellation of Cassiopeia.

With other binaries, the components are much closer together, so that a circling planet would have a complicated orbit and would probably undergo intolerable extremes of temperature. Then, too, there are binaries in which the components are of different colours; it would be strange to see, for instance, a red sun together with a blue one, but in many instances this may well happen. On the whole, however, close binaries do not seem to be promising candidates, and we can presumably rule out the variable stars, because a sun which regularly brightened and faded would produce a very uncomfortable sort of climate upon any planets moving round it.

From a planet orbiting a star inside a globular cluster, the sky would be glorious indeed; there would be many other suns within a radius of a few light-years, and there would be no true darkness at any time. Yet in the long run astronomy on such a world might not benefit, because it would be difficult to see outside the immediate parts of the cluster. Conversely, a planet orbiting a star on the fringe of the Galaxy would have a very dull, barren-looking night sky.

We cannot hope to find out how different races on alien planets have evolved. High surface gravity could well mean the need for extra legs—why should an intelligent creature necessarily be a biped? Other races may be quite unlike ourselves in outward aspect, and each must be suited to its environment. Aquatic intelligences are not improbable upon planets where the surface is largely ocean-covered, and it is certainly true that seals and dolphins are among the most intelligent of all animals on Earth. There may be worlds where the atmosphere is so thin that life is confined to the valleys, and there may be worlds upon which the

most advanced creatures are flyers. I am not
prepared to believe in a hydrogen-breathing monster
of the science fiction type, because all the evidence
is to the contrary, but I am fully prepared to accept
an intelligent being which looks quite unlike a man.
This is not the same principle, because such a being
will be made up of the same materials as ourselves,
and will be an alien only in superficial aspect.

In saying all this, I may have crossed the boundary
between speculation and fantasy, and in any case
there is no point in going further, because as yet we
cannot obtain either confirmation or denial.

There is one more comment worth making, in
rather grim vein. I have already said that on some
planets, evolving civilizations will destroy themselves by nuclear war, and contaminate their world
in the process. Yet it may be that after a sufficient
interval the contamination will wear off; will life
then be re-born, and, if so, will it develop along the
same lines as on the first occasion? There may be
vast numbers of ruined planets circling the stars in
our Galaxy and others, so that the question is
decidedly relevant. We can only hope that Earth
will not add one more world to such a catalogue of
failure.

[6]

The Fate of the Earth

MANKIND IS YOUNG. As has been said several times in this book, our civilization is still in its infancy, and the Earth itself is not half-way through its career; it is more than 4,000 million years old, but in 4,000 million years from now it will probably still exist. Yet it cannot last indefinitely, and its final fate will be bound up with changes in the Sun.

Astronomers of a few decades ago thought that the Sun must have passed its peak, and be gradually shrinking and cooling, so that in the course of time it would become a red dwarf. This would mean a slow but inexorable fall in the Earth's temperature, so that life here would be frozen to death unless it had in the meantime become intelligent enough to take some positive action. However, our views have changed. Instead of cooling down to extinction, the Sun is likely to go through a period of great luminosity, so that heat instead of cold will be Man's ultimate danger.

The Sun is a normal star, producing its energy by the conversion of hydrogen into helium. This is a process that can go on for a very long time, but the supply of hydrogen is not infinite, and there will come a period—perhaps 8,000 to 10,000 million years ahead—when the available hydrogen will start to become exhausted. By then, naturally, the Sun's inner core will consist chiefly of helium.

Without making any attempt to go into details about stellar evolution, it may be said that the probable outcome is a drastic change in the Sun's make-up. Other nuclear processes will take over, involving the conversion of helium into heavier elements; the solar core will shrink, and the outer layers will expand. Though the surface temperature will drop, the globe will swell out, and the total luminosity will increase. Instead of being a hydrogen-burning star, the Sun will have become a Red Giant.

We know of plenty of Red Giants; Betelgeux in Orion is one, Antares in the Scorpion another, and their strong hues are evident at a glance. Instead of being at an early stage in their careers, we now believe them to be very advanced. In their cores, the temperatures reach fantastic values—but their life-expectancies are limited, and when they have used up their main resources they may be expected to collapse into White Dwarfs, bankrupt of all nuclear energy, and shining feebly only because they are still contracting.

This, then, may be the fate of the Sun; from its present state to that of a Red Giant, from Red Giant to White Dwarf, from White Dwarf to ultimate extinction as a luminous body. The details given here may be quite wrong, because theories of stellar evolution seem to be altered every few decades, but they do seem logical. There is always the chance that the Sun will go through a variable star stage, or suffer a nova outburst, in which case life on Earth would be destroyed immediately, but this does not seem probable. For the moment, then, let us assume that the Sun will evolve steadily without flaring up into a nova. What is likely to be the fate of our remote descendants?

There is no imminent peril, as we can see by making up a very crude time-scale. If one 24-hour period represents a million years, then one "day" covers the whole of the Ice Age and much or all of the story of mankind; but the crisis caused by the conversion of the Sun into a Red Giant will lie about 22 years ahead, corresponding to a real period of at least 8,000 million years. It gives us plenty of time to lay our plans.

It does not seem likely that future humanity will change much from a physical point of view, because our bodies, faulty though they may be in many respects, are well suited to our surroundings. Moreover, medical science may be expected to overcome many twentieth-century ills, and by A.D. 3000 a death from cancer will probably be almost unknown, just as a healthy man of A.D. 1968 is unlikely to die from appendicitis even though appendicitis was a killer disease in A.D. 1668. Our descendants may live longer than our own 70 to 90 years, but they will not alter basically. Neither, for that matter, will animals, and there is no suggestion that an ape will develop mentally to the point of mastering the art of coherent speech. Robots will no doubt be perfected, but need not concern us here, simply because a man is a man and a machine is a machine.

Given a prolonged period of peace, science will make strides which we cannot even contemplate as yet. If we have built computers, space-ships and artificial-kidney machines in a mere few minutes according to our time-scale, there is no knowing what we may achieve within the next 22 years.

Social problems as such are outside the scope of this discussion, vitally important though they are (particularly the over-population menace, which will have to be tackled sooner or later). Within a few thousands of years most of the Earth's natural resources, such as coal, will have been used up, but with a non-increasing population and a sensible system of world government this would not matter much, because it seems safe to say that nuclear power will have taken over. Travel between Earth, Moon, perhaps Mars and/or Venus will have been achieved, and explorers may have ventured out to the far regions of the Solar System. We may expect that eventually, civilization will settle down to a stable existence shorn of many of our present difficulties and doubts.

I may be accused of trying to paint a word-picture of Utopia, very pleasant to discuss but quite impossible to attain. Yet I would strongly question this attitude. Given freedom from war and relief from overcrowding, there is no reason whatsoever why mankind should not create something in the nature of a Utopia. The next century or two will show the trend.

If Utopia comes, how long can it persist? Something of the order of 8,000 million years, presumably, but then there must be changes as the Sun starts to rearrange itself for the giant phase of its evolution.

The change will not be sudden by our everyday standards, and will take thousands of years at least, so that there will be a warning which our descendants may be expected to heed. Unfortunately, there is every chance that when the Sun is at its most luminous, and at the peak of its career as a Red Giant, the Earth will be destroyed. At the very least the surface temperature of our world will rise so greatly that the atmosphere will be removed, and no life will survive. Venus, of course, will be in even worse case, and Mars cannot be any salvation.

A civilization which has endured for 8,000 million years will not easily be defeated, and will examine the several possibilities for survival. The most obvious is to migrate to another planet, but it must be remembered that the Sun's Red Giant state will be followed by a collapse into a feeble White Dwarf condition, so that a mass exodus to Mars would provide a solution that would be no more than temporary (even if it were practicable and desirable, which is more than dubious). If interstellar travel has been achieved by that time, there will almost certainly be a general departure from Earth. Alternatively, it just might be possible to adjust the Earth's orbit, forcing it out to a safe distance and then bringing it in once more when the Sun collapses. Neither is it out of the question that nuclear developments would enable humanity to survive on or in the Earth without drawing upon solar power at all.

Once more we are drifting into fantasy—and indeed, when considering events so far ahead it is impossible to do anything else. We have not the faintest notion of what may have happened here before the Sun starts to change, and terrestrial life may have altered out of all recognition, though we may assume that men will still be "men" in the basic meaning of the word.

When we try to see still further into the future, we are back with our problem of trying to picture a time-span that has no ending. We cannot succeed, and for this reason alone we cannot tell whether or not the career of humanity is limited. Eventually it will have to leave the Earth, but this does not necessarily mean that mankind will die out. Across the Galaxy, other intelligent races will be facing similar problems; some of them will undoubtedly find answers. The end of the Earth will not mean the end of life in the universe.

Epilogue

OUR STUDIES OF the universe have been made in a few definite phases. There was the Age of Myth, when men simply looked up at the stars and wondered what they might be. Then came the Age of Arrogance, when the Earth was thought to have been singled out for divine attention, and to be the most important of all bodies. There followed the Age of Humility, when it became clear that our world is totally insignificant. We have entered the Age of Travel, when we are starting to launch out toward our neighbour worlds, though we have already come to realize that our range is painfully limited.

If all goes well, we may pass on to the Age of Enlightenment; but first we must survive the danger-period which began twenty years ago and which is not likely to end for a century or two yet. The Earth can support us for an immense period in the future, provided that we attain intellectual maturity—but if we fail, as many other races in the Galaxy must have failed, then we shall have only ourselves to blame.

Index

233

Light, refraction of, 90–1
Lindemann, F. A., 119
Livy, 48
Local group of galaxies, 145
Lomonosov, M., 73
Lorini, Niccolo, 78
Louis of Bavaria, 42
Lowell, P., 175
Lowell Observatory, 97
Lucian of Samosata, 116
Luther, Martin, 79

Macrinus, Emperor, 45
Malthus, Robert, 206
Mammals, evolution of, 10, 81
Man, future of, 226–9
    origin of, 11–2, 215
Mars, 71, 107–8, 128, 175–7, 179,
    184–6, 215, 220
Martian bases, 207–8
Menes, King, 13, 16
Mercury, 105–6, 111, 174, 180, 208
"Merry Dancers", 50
Messier, C., 141
Meteorites, 89, 181–3
Meteor crater, 181
Meteors, 180
Milky Way, 75, 82
Miller, W., 47
Mizar, 82, 135–6
Moon, 6, 66, 94, 106–7, 111, 174,
    177–9
    bases on, 173, 197, 201–4
    travel to, 125–6
Moulton, F. R., 119
Mount Wilson Observatory, 84,
    93, 142, 165
Mu-mesons, 210–1
Mythology, Greek, 29–30

Neanderthal man, 12
Nebulæ, 83–4, 141–2
Neptune, 59, 109–10, 209
Newcomb, S., 118
Newton, Isaac, 64, 73, 90, 94
Nicias, 41
Novæ, 51, 135
Nuclear tests, 194
Nuclear war, 198–9, 218, 223

Oberth, H., 203
Observatories, modern, 97
    pre-telescopic, 74, 97
Orgueil Meteorite, 183
Orion Nebula, 84, 142
Oscillating universe, 155
Over-population problems,
    205–6, 227
Ozma, Project, 189

Palomar Observatory, 93–4,
    97–8, 103, 145, 155, 165–7, 172
Paris 49-in. refractor, 169
Pericles, 22
Perseid meteors, 180
Perseus legend, 29
Phæthon legend, 29
Phobos, 177
Photography, astronomical, 83
Piazzi Smyth, 18
Pic du Midi Observatory, 167
Piltdown Man, 12–3
Planets, the, 21, 54, 56, 104, 138
    extra-solar, 138–40
Plato, 32–3
Pleiades, 141, 145
Pleistocene period, 11
Pliny, 44
Pluto, 58–9, 104, 114, 175, 209
Polaris, 18, 23, 83
Precession of the Equinoxes, 18,
    27
Procyon, 210
Proxima Centauri, 82, 221
Ptolemy, 15, 26–7, 55–6, 59, 65–7
Pyramids, the, 17–8
Pythagoras, 21, 40

Quasars, 148–50, 157, 165

Radar astronomy, 102–3
Radio astronomy, 98–102
Radio telescopes, lunar, 172
Radioactivity, 4–6
Red Giants, 137, 225
Regulus, 57
Religion, future, 199–200, 219
Rhodesia, sanctions against, 166
Riccioli, 73, 136
Rigel, 83, 190–1